ISNM

INTERNATIONAL SERIES OF NUMERICAL MATHEMATICS
INTERNATIONALE SCHRIFTENREIHE ZUR NUMERISCHEN MATHEMATIK
SÉRIE INTERNATIONALE D'ANALYSE NUMÉRIQUE

VOL. I

INTRODUCTION
TO THE CONSTRUCTIVE THEORY
OF FUNCTIONS

by

JOHN TODD

Professor of Mathematics
California Institute of Technology

1963
ACADEMIC PRESS INC.
NEW YORK

Library of Congress Catalog Card Number 63 - 20576

© Birkhäuser Verlag Basel, 1963
Printed in Switzerland

5

TABLE OF CONTENTS

NOTATIONS AND ABBREVIATIONS

NATANSON (1955)	this refers to the bibliography at the end
$\in$	belongs to
$\Rightarrow$	implies
$\Leftarrow$	is implied by
$\equiv$	equivalent to
[ ]	closed interval
( )	open interval
[ ), ( ]	half-open interval
F.C.	Fourier Coefficients
F.S.	Fourier Series
(C.) N.O.S.	(Complete) normal orthogonal system
$\tilde{p}$	if p is a polynomial $p = k_n x^n + \cdots$ where $k_n \neq 0$ then $\tilde{p} = k_n^{-1} p = x^n + \cdots$ is that multiple of it with leading coefficient unity
$(2n)!! =$	$2 \times 4 \times \cdots (2n-2)(2n)$
$(2n-1)!! =$	$1 \times 3 \times 5 \times \cdots (2n-3)(2n-1)$
$[q] =$	integral part of the real number q
$\delta(m, n) =$	$\begin{cases} 0 & \text{if } m \neq n \\ 1 & m = n \end{cases}$ (Kronecker Symbol)
$\pi_n(x), p_n(x)$	polynomials of degree n
O, o	the usual order symbols
$\mathscr{I}$	the closed interval $[0, 1]$
lub	least upper bound
glb	greatest lower bound
$a(h)\ a + nh$	$a, a + h, a + 2h, \ldots, a + (n-1)h, a + nh$
$\mathscr{R}z$	the real part of the complex number z
$\mathscr{I}z$	the imaginary part of the complex number z
R_n	the n-dimensional enclidean space

PREFACE

The aim of this booklet is at three distinct targets:
(1) To present to prospective mathematicians, an account of some elegant but usually overlooked ideas from classical analysis, which are accessible at an early stage. We hope that this will help to provide them with a balanced view of mathematics, and in particular, show that, at this level there are attractive new ideas in analysis.
(2) To provide a carrier for some mild propaganda for numerical analysis. It must be made clear that this is *not* a main course in numerical analysis, but rather an appetizer or relish. We have included occasional numerical examples, for few scientists are not attracted by striking numerical approximations and computational tours de force. We point out, however, that the clear-cut, best-possible results often available here are in sharp contrast to the necessary vagueness in practical numerical analysis at levels near those of current operations, although these have their own excitements.
(3) To put on record, in a palatable context, some of the basic formulas and properties of the classical orthogonal polynomials, of which most scientists have need from time to time.

We consider that the core of the course is the Chebyshev theory sketched in Chapter 3. A useful preliminary to some of the ideas used in this chapter and Chapter 5 on Orthogonal Polynomials is a familiarity with the theory of Sturm sequences. Although no direct use is made of this theory, a good case could be made for adding some account of this theory and its developments.

We have developed in the text, or in the Problems, the basic formulae concerning the Chebyshev and Legendre Polynomials—the corresponding results for the Laguerre and Hermite cases are recorded without proof.

We have stressed the Aitken Interpolation Algorithm in the problems in Chapter 6—this is a most valuable aid. In Chapter 7, we consider the account of the Euler-Maclaurin Sum Formula and its application to the derivation of the Stirling formula should not be omitted. Chapter 8 gives a brief introduction to Functional Analysis, so that we can present a reasonable proof of the existence of a best Chebyshev approximation. In Chapter 9 the idea of Gaussian quadratures is central. We have put considerable effort into the collection of about 100 examples: the reader is recommended to do the same. Solutions to many are given at the end.

In preparing this printed version we have benefitted from comments by T. K. BOEHME, G. BALEY PRICE, M. LEES and A. SHARPLES, who used the original mimeographed version in courses, and by DIETER GAIER, WALTER GAUTSCHI and J. STEINBERG.   J. T.

INTRODUCTION

The term 'Constructive Theory of Functions' is due to the Russian mathematician S. N. BERNSTEIN (1880). The subject derives from the work of CHEBYSHEV (1821—1894) and his pupils, e. g. KORKINE, ZOLOTAREFF, and the brothers MARKOFF. It was set up as independent discipline by BERNSTEIN to whom and to whose pupils much of its later development is due.

Basically our subject is concerned with the approximate representation of functions in terms of simpler ones, e.g.

(1)   functions $f(x)$, continuous on an interval $[a, b]$, in terms of polynomials

$$\sum_{i=1}^{k} a_i \, x^i$$

or

(2)   functions $F(x)$, continuous on $(-\infty, \infty)$ and periodic with period 2π, in terms of trigonometrical polynomials

$$\sum_{i=0}^{k} (a_i \cos i \, x + b_i \sin i \, x) \; .$$

It is therefore likely to be of considerable use in the various applications, but it also turns out to be an intrinsically interesting area of mathematics which includes many sharp and appealing results which are easily accessible.

The standard work in this field is the treatise of NATANSON (1955), published in Russian in 1951, but now available in translations.

Some aspects of our subject are covered in the collection of papers by LANGER (1959); in particular we mention the expository articles of BUCK (1959) and TODD (1959). A condensed account is given in TODD (1962).

We require some background material from algebra and the foundations of analysis. This is summarized in Chapter 1 and can be found in such texts as APOSTOL (1957), BIRKHOFF and MacLANE (1953), and OSTROWSKI (1952—1954).

CHAPTER 1

Results from Algebra and Analysis

We state here some of the basic facts which will be required later.

(**1.1**) *Every polynomial has a zero.*
This is the Fundamental Theorem of Algebra; from it we deduce the following:

(**1.2**) *A polynomial of degree n has at most n zeros.*

(**1.3**) *A polynomial of degree n is determined uniquely by its values at n + 1 distinct points, $x_0, x_1, \ldots, x_n$.*

Proofs:
(1) (LAGRANGE). We introduce the following notation:

$$w_i(x) = \prod_{j \neq i} (x - x_j), \quad l_i(x) = \frac{w_i(x)}{w_i(x_i)}, \quad i = 0, 1, \ldots, n.$$

Then $w_i(x)$ and $l_i(x)$ are polynomials of degree n and $l_i(x_i) = 1$, $l_i(x_j) = 0$, $i \neq j$. Hence

$$L_n(f, x) \equiv \sum_{i=0}^{n} f_i l_i(x)$$

is a polynomial of degree n assuming the values f_i at the points x_i. That it is the only such polynomial follows from (**1.2**). This proof has a constructive character.

(2) (VANDERMONDE). Assume

$$p_n(x) \equiv a_0 x^n + \cdots + a_{n-1} x + a_n.$$

Then the set of $n + 1$ linear equations in the $n + 1$ unknowns $a_0, \ldots, a_n$

$$p_n(x_i) = f_i, \quad i = 0, 1, \ldots, n$$

has a solution: the determinant of the system is a Vandermondian and does not vanish since the x_i are distinct. This proof is more in the nature of an existence theorem.
The differences of a function $f(x)$, at interval h, are defined as follows:

$$\Delta f(x) = f(x + h) - f(x),$$

$$\Delta^{n+1} f(x) = \Delta(\Delta^n f(x)), \quad n \geq 1.$$

If it is necessary to indicate the interval h, a subscript can be attached to the Δ. We call $\Delta^n f(x)$ the *n-th (forward) difference* of $f(x)$. For any n, Δ^n is manifestly a *linear operator*: $\Delta^n(a\, A(x) + b\, B(x)) = a\, \Delta^n A(x) + b\, \Delta^n B(x)$.

(1.4) *The n-th differences of a polynomial of degree n are constant, and the $(n+1)$st differences are zero, the differences being taken at any fixed interval h.*

Proof: By induction.

We presuppose some account of the real number system and shall make use of the following theorems, among others.

(1.5) *A set of real numbers which is bounded above (below) has a least upper (greatest lower) bound.*

(1.6) *A bounded monotone sequence has a limit.*

(1.7) (BOLZANO-WEIERSTRASS). *A bounded infinite set has a limit point.*

(1.8) (BOREL). *If a bounded closed interval can be covered by a set of open intervals, then it can be covered by a finite sub-system.*

We require the idea of continuity of a function of a real variable: $f(x)$ is *continuous at* x_0 if given any $\varepsilon > 0$, there is a $\delta = \delta(\varepsilon, x_0)$ such that if $|x - x_0| < \delta$ then $|f(x) - f(x_0)| < \varepsilon$. The following results are needed.

(1.9) *A function continuous on a bounded closed interval is bounded there; further, it assumes its bounds.*

(1.10) (BOLZANO). *If $f(x)$ is continuous in $[a, b]$ and if $f(a)$ and $f(b)$ have different signs, there is a point between a and b at which $f(x)$ vanishes.*

(1.11) (HEINE). *If $f(x)$ is continuous in a bounded closed interval $[a, b]$ it is uniformly continuous there, i.e., given $\varepsilon > 0$ we can find a $\delta = \delta(\varepsilon)$ such that if $|x' - x''| < \delta$, $a \leq x', x'' \leq b$ then $|f(x') - f(x'')| < \varepsilon$.*

(1.12) (ROLLE). *If $f(x)$ is continuous in $[a, b]$, if $f(a) = 0$, $f(b) = 0$ and if $f'(x)$ exists in (a, b) then there is a point c in (a, b) such that $f'(c) = 0$.*

We make use of the idea of a *limit of a sequence*, (or, equivalently, the *sum of an infinite series*): $\lim S_n = S$ if given any $\varepsilon > 0$ there is an $n_0 = n_0(\varepsilon)$ such that if $n \geq n_0$ then $|S - S_n| < \varepsilon$. We write

$$u_0 + u_1 + \cdots = \sum_{r=0}^{\infty} u_r = S$$

if

$$\lim S_n = S$$

where

$$S_n = u_0 + u_1 + \cdots + u_n .$$

We use the following results.

(1.13)   *A series with positive terms is convergent if and only if the sequence of its partial sums is bounded.*

(1.14)   (LEIBNIZ). *An alternating series*

$$\sum_{0}^{\infty} (-1)^n u_n$$

is convergent if $u_0 \geq u_1 \geq u_2 \geq \cdots$ *and* $u_n \to 0$.

A convergent sequence whose terms $S_n(x)$ depend on a parameter x is said to *converge uniformly with respect to that parameter* if given $\varepsilon > 0$ we can choose an $n_0 = n_0(\varepsilon)$ *independent* of x such that if $n \geq n_0$ then $|S(x) - S_n(x)| < \varepsilon$, all relevant x. We define *uniform convergence of a series* $\sum u_n(x)$ similarly. A very simple condition sufficient to ensure that $\sum u_n(x)$ is uniformly convergent is the following.

(1.15)   (WEIERSTRASS M-Test). $\sum u_n(x)$ *is uniformly convergent if there is a convergent series* $\sum M_n$, *such that*

$$|u_n(x)| \leq M_n, \quad n = 0, 1, 2, \ldots$$

for all relevant x.

Suppose a series $\sum u_n(x)$ is uniformly convergent in $[a, b]$. If we can integrate each term then we can integrate 'term by term', i.e.,

(1.16)
$$\int_a^x \sum u_n(t)\, dt = \sum \int_a^x u_n(t)\, dt$$

for x in $[a, b]$; moreover the series on the right is uniformly convergent in $[a, b]$. If each term $u_n(x)$ is continuous at x_0 then we can pass to the limit 'term by term':

(1.17)
$$\lim_{x \to x_0} \sum u_n(x) = \sum \left\{ \lim_{x \to x_0} u_n(x) \right\}.$$

We shall make use of the Mean Value Theorem of the Differential Calculus:

(1.18)   *If $f(x)$ is continuous in $[a, b]$ and if $f'(x)$ exists in (a, b), then there is a point ζ, $a < \zeta < b$, such that*

$$f(b) - f(a) = (b - a)\, f'(\zeta),$$

and of the Taylor Theorem, one form of which we state:

(1.19)   (TAYLOR). *If $f^{(n+1)}(x)$ is continuous in $[a, x]$ then*

$$f(x) = f(a) + \frac{(x-a)}{1!}\, f'(a) + \frac{(x-a)^2}{2!}\, f''(a) + \cdots + \frac{(x-a)^n}{n!}\, f^{(n)}(a) + R_{n+1}$$

where

$$R_{n+1} = \int_a^x \frac{(x-t)^n}{n!} \, f^{(n+1)}(t) \, dt \, .$$

We shall also require the Mean Value Theorem of the Integral Calculus:

(1.20) (DIRICHLET). *If $f(x)$ and $w(x)$ are continuous in $[a, b]$ and if $w(x) \geq 0$, $a \leq x \leq b$, then there is a point ζ, $a \leq \zeta \leq b$, such that*

$$\int_a^b f(x) \, w(x) \, dx = f(\zeta) \int_a^b w(x) \, dx \, .$$

Chapter 1. Problems

1.1. Express the general term of the following series in partial fractions

$$\sum_{n=0}^{\infty} \frac{1}{(n + x + 1)(n + x + 2)}$$

and hence find its sum and the remainder after n terms, $R_n(x)$. Find the least value of $n_0 = n_0(x, \varepsilon)$ such that

$$|R_n(x)| < \varepsilon$$

for $\varepsilon = 0.05$, $x = 10, 1, 0.1, 0.01, 0.001, 0$.

1.2 (STOKES). The same as **Problem 1.1,** but for the series

$$\sum_{n=1}^{\infty} \frac{x(x+2)n^2 + x(4-x)n + 1 - x}{n(n+1)((n-1)x+1)(nx+1)} \,.$$

1.3 For $n = 0, 1, 2, \ldots$ let $\varepsilon_n = 2^{-n}$, denote by P_n the points $(\varepsilon_n, 0)$, denote by Q_{2n} the points $(\varepsilon_{2n}, \varepsilon_n)$.

Let $f(x)$ be the function whose graph, for $0 \le x \le 1$, consists the broken line $Q_0 P_1 Q_2 P_3 Q_4 \ldots$ and the origin.

(1) Is $f(x)$ a polygonal function, $0 \le x \le 1$?
(2) Is $f(x)$ a continuous function, $0 \le x \le 1$?
(3) Is $f(x)$ uniformly continuous in $0 \le x \le 1$?
(4, 5, 6) the same as (1, 2, 3) for the interval $\varepsilon \le x \le 1$ where $0 < \varepsilon < 1$.
[Justify your answers from first principles, not by quoting theorems; by a *polygonal function* we understand one whose graph is a set of straight lines $R_0 R_1, R_1 R_2, \ldots, R_{n-1} R_n$ where R_r is a point (a_r, b_r), $r = 0, 1, \ldots, n$.]

1.4 Show from first principles that a polynomial is uniformly continuous on any bounded interval.

1.5 (DE RHAM). Denote by $[y]$ the greatest integer which does not exceed y. Draw the graph of $u_0 = \phi(x) = |x - [x + (1/2)]|$. Draw the graph of $u_1 = (1/2)\phi(2x)$. Draw the graph of $u_2 = (1/4)\phi(4x)$. Draw the graph $u^3 = 2^{-3}\phi(2^3 x)$.

Draw the graphs of $u_0 + u_1$, $u_0 + u_1 + u_2$, $u_0 + u_1 + u_2 + u_3$. Can you make any guesses about the behavior of the series

$$\sum_{k=0}^{\infty} 2^{-k}\phi(2^k x) \,?$$

Does it converge? Does it converge uniformly? If it has a sum function $\Phi(x)$, is $\Phi(x)$ continuous? Is $\Phi(x)$ differentiable?

Show that $\Phi(x)$ satisfies the functional equation

$$\Phi(x) - \frac{1}{2}\Phi(2x) = \phi(x) \,.$$

1.6   If the interval $h = 1$, show that

$$\Delta^n f(0) = f(n) - \binom{n}{1} f(n-1) + \binom{n}{2} f(n-2) + \cdots + (-1)^n f(0) .$$

1.7   Compute $\Delta^n \binom{x}{\nu}$, for $n = 1, 2, \ldots$ and $\nu = 1, 2, \ldots$, the differencing being with respect to x, at interval 1. [The binomial coefficient $\binom{x}{\nu}$ is defined to be

$$\frac{x(x-1) \cdots (x - \nu + 1)}{1 \times 2 \times \cdots \times \nu}$$

for any x and any integer $\nu \geq 1$; if $\nu = 0$ the binomial coefficient is defined to be 1 for any x.]

1.8   (NEWTON). Prove that

$$p_n(x) = a_0 \binom{x}{0} + a_1 \binom{x}{1} + \cdots + a_n \binom{x}{n}$$

is a polynomial of degree n such that

$$p_n(\mu) = f(\mu) , \quad \mu = 0, 1, 2, \ldots, n ,$$

provided that

$$a_\mu = \binom{\mu}{0} f(\mu) - \binom{\mu}{1} f(\mu - 1) + \cdots + (-1)^\mu \binom{\mu}{\mu} f(0) ,$$

for $\mu = 0, 1, 2, \ldots, n$.

1.9   Evaluate

$$B_n(f, x) = \sum_{k=0}^{n} \binom{n}{k} x^k (1-x)^{n-k} f\left(\frac{k}{n}\right)$$

when $f = 1$, $f = x$, $f = x^2$, $f = x^3$.

1.10   Show that the coefficient of x^k in $B_n(f, x)$ is

$$\binom{n}{k} \Delta^k f(0) ,$$

where the differences are taken at interval $h = n^{-1}$.

1.11   Show that

$$\sum_{k=0}^{n} \binom{n}{k} p^k q^{n-k} (k - n p) = 0$$

where $p + q = 1$.

1.12   Show that

$$\sum_{k=0}^{n} \binom{n}{k} p^k q^{n-k} (k - n p)^2 = n p q$$

where $p + q = 1$.

[Hint for **Problems 1.11-12**: differentiate the identity

$$\sum \binom{n}{k} p^k\, q^{n-k} = (p+q)^n$$

with respect to p, regarding p, q as independent variables.]

1.13 If

$$S_m(p) = \sum_{k=0}^{n} \binom{n}{k} p^k\, q^{n-k}\, (k - n\, p)^m$$

obtain a three-term recurrence relation for $S_m(p)$ and use it, and the previous two results, to evaluate $S_3(p)$, $S_4(p)$.

1.14 Denote by $R_n(x)$ the remainder in the infinite series in **Problem 1.1**. Evaluate

$$M_n = \underset{0 \le x < \infty}{\text{lub}} \; \big| R_n(x) \big| .$$

1.15 The same as **Problem 1.14** for the series in **Problem 1.2**.

1.16 Show that each of the following two conditions is necessary and sufficient for the uniform convergence of a series $\sum u_n(x)$, convergent for all $x \in X$. Let $R_n(x)$ denote the remainder after n terms in this series.
   (1) Let $m(\varepsilon, x)$ be the least integer n such that

$$\big| R_n(x) \big| < \varepsilon, \quad \text{if} \quad n \ge m(\varepsilon, x) .$$

Condition (1). $\underset{x \in X}{\text{lub}} \; m(\varepsilon, x)$ finite for all ε.
   (2) Let

$$M_n = \underset{x \in X}{\text{lub}} \; \big| R_n(x) \big| .$$

Condition (2). M_n is a null sequence.

1.17 Evaluate det W where $W_{ij} = \omega^{ij}$, $i, j = 1, 2, \ldots, n$, and ω is a primitive complex n-th root of unity.

1.18 If $x_1, x_2, \ldots, x_n$ are unequal and are the zeros of a polynomial $\pi_n(x)$, show that in the Lagrangian interpolant

$$L_n(f, x) = L_{\pi_n}(f, x) = \sum f_i\, l_i(x)$$

we have

$$l_i(x) = \pi_n(x)/[\pi_n'(x_i)\, (x - x_i)] .$$

1.19 (BERNSTEIN). If $f(x)$ is continuous in $[a, b]$, if $f(a) = 0$, $f(b) = 0$, then the difference

$$\Delta_h\, f(x) = f(x + h) - f(x)$$

has a zero in this interval, provided h is sufficiently small.

1.20   TAYLOR's Theorem with the remainder in the Lagrangian form states that

$$f(x + h) = f(x) + h f'(x) + \cdots + \frac{h^{n-1}}{(n-1)!} f^{(n-1)}(x) + \frac{h^n}{n!} f^{(n)}(x + \theta_n h) .$$

Show that if $f, f', \ldots, f^{(n+2)}$ are continuous and $f^{(n+1)}(x) \neq 0$ then

$$\theta_n = \frac{1}{n+1} + \frac{n h}{2(n+1)^2 (n+2)} \left\{ \frac{f^{(n+2)}(x)}{f^{(n+1)}(x)} + o(1) \right\}$$

as $h \to 0$.

CHAPTER 2

The Theorems of Weierstrass

(2.1) *If $f(x)$ is continuous in $[a, b]$ then given any $\varepsilon > 0$ there is a polynomial $p = p_\varepsilon(x)$ such that*

$$\left| f(x) - p(x) \right| \le \varepsilon, \quad a \le x \le b.$$

This was established by WEIERSTRASS in 1885. Another form of this is:

(2.2) *If $f(x)$ is continuous in $[a, b]$ there is a series of polynomials $\sum q_n(x)$ which is uniformly convergent to $f(x)$ in $[a, b]$.*

There are analogous theorems for continuous functions which are periodic in an interval which we can take to be $[0, 2\pi]$. These can be established directly, or indirectly by showing that they are equivalent to the above results. The analogue of **(2.1)** is:

(2.3) *If $F(\theta)$ is a function continuous in $(-\infty, \infty)$ which has period 2π, then given any $\varepsilon > 0$ there is a trigonometrical polynomial $T = T_\varepsilon$:*

$$T(\theta) = \frac{1}{2} a_0 + \sum_{r=1}^{n} (a_r \cos r\theta + b_r \sin r\theta),$$

such that

$$\left| F(\theta) - T(\theta) \right| \le \varepsilon,$$

all θ.

There are many proofs of these theorems. We describe briefly two of the simpler ones due to LEBESGUE (1898) and to LANDAU (1908) but shall concentrate on that of BERNSTEIN (1912).

The proof that **(2.1)** $\equiv$ **(2.2)** is easy. It is also easy to show that **(2.3)** $\equiv$ **(2.1)**. For a proof of **(2.1)** via **(2.3)**, see APOSTOL (1957).

Lebesgue's Proof of (2.1). We note that, in virtue of uniform continuity, we can approximate $f(x)$ arbitrarily closely by a *polygonal* function. We can represent such a polygonal function as a linear combination of polynomials and distorted functions $|x|$. The distortion consists in a change of origin and of scale: $a \, | x - b |$. The problem is therefore reduced to that of approximating $|x|$ by polynomials. This is done by noticing that

$$|x| = \sqrt{1 - (1 - x^2)}$$

and expanding the right hand side as a binomial series

$$1 - \frac{1}{2} (1 - x^2) - \frac{1}{8} (1 - x^2)^2 - \cdots.$$

Todd 2

There is some difficulty about the behavior of this at $x = 0$. This can be overcome by a careful analysis of the convergence of the series at $x = 0$. This can be done by examining the ratio of consecutive terms of the series, or preferably, by a direct discussion of the remainder in the Maclaurin series

$$(1 - t)^{1/2} = 1 - \frac{1}{2} t - \frac{1}{8} t^2 - \cdots - \frac{1 \times 3 \cdots (2n - 3)}{2 \times 4 \cdots 2n} t^n$$

$$+ \frac{t^{n+1}}{n!} \int_0^1 \left[\left(\frac{d}{d(tx)} \right)^{n+1} (1 - tx)^{1/2} \right] (1 - x)^n \, dx .$$

An alternative, more elementary (but more complicated) treatment is possible. See Ostrowski (1951), p. 168.

Landau's Proof of (2.1). This depends on the use of a singular integral (delta function). Consider, in the case $a = 0$, $b = 1$,

$$I_n(\delta) = \int_\delta^1 (1 - z^2)^n \, dz , \quad 0 \le \delta \le 1 .$$

It is plausible, from consideration of the graphs of $y = x^n$, that $I_n(\delta)$ is negligible with respect to $I_n(0)$: the area represented by $I_n(0)$ is concentrated near $\delta = 0$. It can indeed be shown that for $\delta > 0$

$$I_n(\delta)/I_n(0) \to 0$$

as $n \to \infty$.
   This suggests that

$$(2 I_n(0))^{-1} \int_0^1 f(z) \left(1 - (z - x)^2 \right)^n \, dz \to f(x) .$$

This can be proved. Further the left hand side is a polynomial in x. This is essentially the result required.
   This proof makes use of the integral calculus but it is not difficult to avoid this. See Landau (1950).

de la Vallée Poussin's Proof of (2.3). This is similar to that of Landau. If

$$V_n(F, \theta) = \frac{(2n)!!}{2\pi(2n - 1)!!} \int_{-\pi}^{+\pi} F(\phi) \cos^{2n} \frac{1}{2} (\phi - \theta) \, d\phi$$

then $V_n(F, \theta) \to F(\theta)$ uniformly.

Bernstein's Proof of (2.1). This proof is best motivated from elementary considerations of probability. The proof however does not depend on any probability ideas and indeed, rather serves to justify these ideas.
   Consider repeated, independent experiments with two possible outcomes: H or T, for which the probabilities are x, $1 - x$ respectively. It is reason-

able to suppose that in a large number n of experiments there will be approximately $x\,n$ successes, $(1 - x)\,n$ failures. Now by elementary reasoning we know that the probability of exactly k successes is

$$p_{nk} = \binom{n}{k} x^k (1 - x)^{n-k} .$$

This quantity, regarded as a function of k, with n, x fixed, should have a high peak where $k \doteq n\,x$, and fall off rapidly on either side. This suggests that although

$$\sum_{k=0}^{n} p_{nk} = 1 ,$$

the sum over the k close to nx will be close to 1, and the sum of the remaining p_{nk} will be near zero.

With these thoughts in mind we consider the Bernstein polynomials for $f(x)$:

$$B_n(f, x) = \sum p_{nk} f(k/n) ,$$

and it follows that, f being continuous, the right hand side should be nearly $f(k/n) \doteq f(x)$, and the approximation should improve as n increases.

We shall now begin afresh and establish the following result rigorously.

(2.4) (BERNSTEIN). *If $f(x)$ is continuous in $[0, 1]$ then*

$$B_n(f, x) = \sum p_{nk} f(k/n) \to f(x)$$

uniformly in $[0, 1]$.

As lemmas we require the results of **Problems 1.11** and **1.12**.

(2.5) $$\sum p_{nk} (k - n\,x) = 0 .$$

(2.6) $$\sum p_{nk} (k - n\,x)^2 = n\,x\,(1 - x) .$$

We shall now establish a third lemma (essentially the Chebyshev inequality).

(2.7) *If $\delta > 0$, then $\sum' p_{nk} < x\,(1 - x)/(n\,\delta^2)$ if $\sum'$ is the sum over those k for which*

$$\left| \frac{k}{n} - x \right| \geq \delta .$$

Proof: Consider the summation in **(2.6)**. Break it up into $\sum'$ and a complementary $\sum''$. We have

$$n\,x\,(1 - x) = \sum' p_{nk} (k - n\,x)^2 + \sum'' p_{nk} (k - n\,x)^2$$
$$\geq \sum' p_{nk} (k - n\,x)^2$$
$$\geq \sum' p_{nk} \times n^2 \delta^2 .$$

The first inequality follows because each term in $\sum$ and therefore in $\sum''$ is essentially non-negative. The second inequality follows because by definition of $\sum'$ we have $|k - n x| \geq n \delta$. Hence

$$\sum{}' p_{nk} \leq x (1 - x)/(n \delta^2) .$$

Remembering that $0 \leq x (1 - x) \leq 1/4$ we conclude that if $n > (4 \delta^2 \varepsilon)^{-1}$ then

$$\sum{}'' p_{nk} > 1 - \varepsilon , \qquad \sum{}' p_{nk} < \varepsilon \tag{2.1}$$

(this is the precise form of the italicized statement on lines 9-10, page 19).

In order to prove (2.4), since $\sum p_{nk} = 1$, it will be sufficient to show that

$$e_n(x) = B_n(f, x) - f(x) = \sum_{k=0}^{n} \left[f \left(\frac{k}{n} \right) - f(x) \right] \left[\binom{n}{k} x^k (1 - x)^{n-k} \right]$$

tends uniformly to zero. We do this by breaking up the sum into $\sum'$ and $\sum''$ and showing that each part, separately, tends uniformly to zero: the first because $\sum' p_{nk}$ is small and $f \left(\frac{k}{n} \right) - f(x)$ is bounded, the second because although $\sum'' p_{nk}$ is near unity, since f is continuous, $f \left(\frac{k}{n} \right)$ is near $f(x)$.

Take any $\varepsilon > 0$. Then choose δ such that

$$| f(x') - f(x'') | < \frac{1}{2} \varepsilon \quad \text{if} \quad | x' - x'' | < \delta , \quad 0 \leq x' , x'' \leq 1 .$$

(This is *uniform* continuity.) Let

$$M = \max_{0 \leq x \leq 1} | f(x) | .$$

Using (2.1) we have

$$| e_n(x) | \leq \sum{}' | f(k/n) - f(x) | p_{nk} + \sum{}'' | f(k/n) - f(x) | p_{nk}$$

$$\leq 2 M \sum{}' p_{nk} + \frac{1}{2} \varepsilon \sum{}'' p_{nk}$$

$$\leq 2 M (4 n \delta^2)^{-1} + \frac{1}{2} \varepsilon .$$

To get the last inequality we have used the fact that

$$\sum{}'' p_{nk} \leq \sum p_{nk} = 1 .$$

If $n \geq M \varepsilon^{-1} \delta^{-2}$, then the first term in the last inequality does not exceed $\varepsilon/2$ and we conclude that

$$| e_n(x) | \leq \varepsilon , \quad \text{all } x, \quad n \geq M \varepsilon^{-1} \delta^{-2} .$$

This completes the proof of (2.4).

Clearly (2.4) $\Rightarrow$ (2.1). It can also be shown that (2.1) $\Rightarrow$ (2.4) using **Problem 1.10**.

Remarks

(a) There are many generalizations of WEIERSTRASS' Theorem. Axiomatic accounts have been given by BOURBAKI and STONE (1948).

A simple extension is to the case of functions of two real variables. For an interesting discussion of civilized and uncivilized proofs of this see LITTLEWOOD (1953).

(b) It is fairly clear that the $B_n(f, x)$ in general will not give the 'best approximation' to $f(x)$, of all polynomials of degree n. Indeed we have seen (**Problem 1.9**)

$$B_n(x^2, x) = x^2 + x(1 - x)/n$$

whereas the best approximation, in any reasonable sense, to x^2 by a polynomial of degree $n \geq 2$ should be x^2 itself. This degree of approximation

$$B_n(x^2, x) - x^2 = O(n^{-1})$$

is typical. This has been established by WORONOWSKAJA in 1932.

(**2.8**) *If $f(x)$ is continuous in $[0, 1]$ and if $f''(x)$ exists for some x, $0 \leq x \leq 1$, then*

$$\lim n \, [f(x) - B_n(f, x)] = -\frac{1}{2} x(1 - x) f''(x) \, .$$

We shall not give the proof of this. See LORENTZ (1953).

The weakness of the Bernstein polynomials as a means for approximation is underlined by comparing this result with consequences of **Problem 3.12**.

(c) We observe that it is not possible to establish the Weierstrass Theorem by means of the Lagrange interpolation formula. Even if the nodes are equally spaced in an interval $[a, b]$, it is not in general true that

$$L_n(f, x) \rightarrow f(x)$$

uniformly in $[a, b]$.

This is false even for such simple functions as $f(x) = |x|$ or $f(x) = (1 + x^2)^{-1}$. See Chapter 6 below.

Chapter 2. Problems

2.1 Evaluate the de la Vallée Poussin integrals:

$$V_n(F, \theta) = \frac{(2n)!!}{2\pi(2n-1)!!} \int_{-\pi}^{+\pi} F(\phi) \cos^{2n} \frac{1}{2}(\phi - \theta)\, d\phi$$

for some simple periodic functions $F(\theta)$, e.g. $F(\theta) = |\cos\theta|$.

2.2 Express the de la Vallée Poussin integral

$$V_n(F, \theta) = \frac{(2n)!!}{2\pi(2n-1)!!} \int_{-\pi}^{+\pi} F(\phi) \cos^{2n} \frac{1}{2}(\phi - \theta)\, d\phi$$

explicitly as a trigonometrical polynomial

$$V_n = \frac{1}{2} A_0 + \sum_{r=1}^{n} [A_r \cos r\theta + B_r \sin r\theta]$$

and find the ratios of A_r, B_r to the corresponding Fourier coefficients a_r, b_r of $F(\theta)$, where

$$a_r = \pi^{-1} \int_{-\pi}^{\pi} F(\phi) \cos r\phi\, d\phi, \quad b_r = \pi^{-1} \int_{-\pi}^{\pi} F(\phi) \sin r\phi\, d\phi.$$

2.3 Evaluate $B_n(e^x, x)$ and check the convergence and convergence rate directly say, when $0 \le x \le 1$.

2.4 (CHLODOVSKY). Show that it is possible, given any function $f(x)$ continuous in an interval $[a, b]$, $0 < a < b < 1$, to find a sequence of polynomials $p_n(x)$, with *integral* coefficients, such that

$$p_n(x) \to f(x)$$

uniformly in $[a, b]$.

2.5 If $m \le f(x) \le M$, show that $m \le B_n(f, x) \le M$.

2.6 Show that the remainder R_n in the binomial series for $(1 - (1 - t^2))^{1/2}$ satisfies

$$|R_n| < \frac{1}{2} \frac{1 \times 3 \cdots (2n-1)}{2 \times 4 \cdots (2n)} \int_0^1 \frac{dx}{\sqrt{1-x}},$$

for all t, $|t| \le 1$.

Show that $R_n \to 0$ by noting that

$$\frac{2n-1}{2n} = 1 - \frac{1}{2n}$$

and that

$$-\log\left(1 - \frac{1}{2n}\right) > \frac{1}{2n},$$

or by using the fact that

$$\left(\frac{1 \times 3 \cdots (2n-1)}{2 \times 4 \cdots (2n)}\right)^2 = \frac{1 \times (2n-1)}{(2n)(2n)} \prod_{r=1}^{n-1}\left\{\frac{(2r-1)(2r+1)}{(2r)(2r)}\right\} < \frac{1}{2n} \ .$$

2.7   Let f be the function whose graph is the polygonal curve connecting

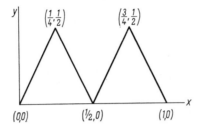

the points $(0, 0)$, $(\frac{1}{4}, \frac{1}{2})$, $(\frac{1}{2}, 0)$, $(\frac{3}{4}, \frac{1}{2})$, and $(1, 0)$ as shown in the figure. Find $B_2(f, x)$ and $B_4(f, x)$ and sketch the graphs of these two polynomials.

2.8   (STRANG). Let f be defined on $[0, 1]$. First interpolate linearly in each subinterval $[m/n, (m+1)/n]$ to get values at the points $(m+x)/n$, $m = 0, 1, \ldots, n-1$. Then interpolate linearly in each subinterval $[(m+x)/n, (m+1+x)/n]$ to get values at the points $(m+2x)/n$, $m = 0, 1, \ldots, n-2$. Continue this process until we obtain a single value by interpolation in $[(n-1)x/n, \{1+(n-1)x\}/n]$ for a value at x. What is this value?

CHAPTER 3

The Chebyshev Theory

In Chapter 2, we have seen that given any function $f(x)$, continuous in $[a, b]$, and any $\varepsilon > 0$, there is a polynomial $p = p_\varepsilon$ such that

$$\left| f(x) - p(x) \right| \leq \varepsilon , \quad a \leq x \leq b .$$

It is natural to ask, for any integer n, what is the polynomial of degree at most n, which is the best approximation to a given $f(x)$? Indeed we should first ask is there a best approximation, and secondly, is it unique?

We shall deal with a special case first: the approximation of $f(x) \equiv 0$ by a $p_n(x)$ or, what is the same thing, the approximation of x^n by a polynomial of lower degree. We shall establish:

(3.1) *Let $\tilde{p}_n(x) = x^n + a_1 x^{n-1} + \cdots + a_n$. Let*

$$\mu(\tilde{p}_n) = \max_{-1 \leq x \leq 1} \left| \tilde{p}_n(x) \right| .$$

Then

$$\mu(\tilde{p}_n) \geq \mu_n = 2^{1-n} .$$

There is equality if and only if

$$\tilde{p}_n = \tilde{T}_n(x) = 2^{1-n} \cos (n \arccos x) .$$

Proof. We note that $\tilde{T}_n = \pm\, 2^{1-n}$, *alternately* at the points

$$x_\nu = \cos \nu \, \pi / n , \quad \nu = 0, 1, \ldots, n .$$

Suppose there was a $\tilde{p}_n(x)$, say $\tilde{\pi}_n(x)$, such that

$$\mu(\tilde{\pi}_n) < \mu_n . \tag{3.1}$$

Consider

$$r = \tilde{T}_n - \tilde{\pi}_n .$$

This is a polynomial of degree $n - 1$ which does not vanish identically. (If it did then $\mu(\tilde{\pi}_n) = \mu(\tilde{T}_n) = \mu_n$, contradicting our supposition.) Now consider the values of r at the points x_ν. Clearly r has alternate signs at these points. (Since $\left| \tilde{\pi}_n \right| < \mu_n$, the sign of r is that of $\tilde{T}_n$.) By ROLLE's Theorem r must vanish between consecutive x_ν, i.e., n times in all—which implies, since it is a polynomial of degree $n - 1$, that it vanishes identically. This is a contradiction. Hence (3.1) is false. Hence

$$\mu(\tilde{p}_n) \geq \mu_n = 2^{1-n} .$$

The proof of the equality results is left as an exercise.

We shall now show that $\tilde{T}_n(x)$ has some compensation for having the smallest deviation from zero within $[-1, 1]$: it is the largest polynomial of its kind outside $[-1, 1]$.

(3.2)   *Let $p_n(x)$ be a polynomial of degree at most n. Let*

$$M = \max_{-1 \leq x \leq 1} |p_n(x)| .$$

Then for any real $\zeta, |\zeta| > 1$, we have

$$|p_n(\zeta)| \leq M |T_n(\zeta)| , \quad where \quad T_n(x) = \cos(n \arccos x) .$$

Proof. Suppose the conclusion is false and consider

$$\pi(x) = [p_n(\zeta) T_n(x)/T_n(\zeta)] - p_n(x) .$$

(This makes sense since $T_n(\zeta)$ is not zero: all the zeros of $T_n(x)$ are in $[-1, 1]$.)

This is a polynomial of degree at most n and $\pi(\zeta) = 0$. Further, since $|p_n(\zeta)/T_n(\zeta)| > M$, and since $T_n(\cos i\,\pi/n) = (-1)^i$, $i = 0, \ldots, n$, it follows that

$$\pi(\cos i\pi/n) = (-1)^i [p_n(\zeta)/T_n(\zeta)] - p_n(\cos i\pi/n)$$

has opposite signs for consecutive i, $|p_n(x)|$ being bounded by M in $[-1, 1]$. Hence π has n zeros inside $[-1, 1]$ and another zero outside, at $x = \zeta$. Hence $\pi(x) \equiv 0$. Hence

$$p_n(x) = p_n(\zeta) T_n(x)/T_n(\zeta) ,$$

so that

$$p_n(1) = p_n(\zeta)/T_n(\zeta) ,$$

and so

$$|p_n(1)| > M$$

—a contradiction.

We shall now discuss the existence of a polynomial of best approximation of any given degree. We write

$$E(p_n) = \max_{a \leq x \leq b} |f(x) - p_n(x)| .$$

Clearly $E(p_n) \geq 0$. Consider the set of all $E(p_n)$, where the p_n varies over all polynomials of degree n at most. This is a set of non-negative real numbers and therefore has a non-negative greatest lower bound E_n such that

$$E(p_n) \geq E_n$$

for all p_n. It is clear that as n increases we introduce more functions into the competition and so the greatest lower bound cannot increase, i.e., $E_1 \geq E_2 \geq \geq \cdots$. This sequence necessarily tends to zero, by the Weierstrass Theorem; how fast it does depends on the behavior of $f(x)$.

We cannot yet assert that for any fixed n this greatest lower bound is attained, i.e., that there is at least one $p_n(x)$ for which

$$E(p_n) = E_n ,$$

nor can we assert that an extremal polynomial is unique. These facts can, however, be established.

(3.3) (BOREL). *If $f(x)$ is continuous in $[a, b]$ then, for each n, there exists a polynomial (of degree $\leq n$) of best approximation.*

We shall prove this theorem in Chapter 8.

The existence of a best approximating polynomial being established, it is natural to ask how to obtain this in any given case. What one would like is a finite algorithm. Such an algorithm exists in the case when we consider mean square approximation (cf. Chapter 5). In the present case, however, no such algorithm is known so far. In some very special cases: e.g. linear approximation to a convex or concave function, results are available.

We shall now discuss a characteristic property of a polynomial of best approximation, and we shall, incidentally, show that the polynomial is unique.

We take a fixed f and any polynomial of best approximation to it, say $p_n(x)$. Then

$$E_n = E(p_n) .$$

We may assume $E(p_n) > 0$ for, if not, then f would be a polynomial of degree at most n. Consider

$$\left| f(x) - p_n(x) \right| .$$

This is continuous in $[a, b]$ and so assumes its maximum E_n in at least one point. Such a point will be called an e-point (e for extremal). We classify the e-points into $\sharp$-points and $\flat$-points according as

$$f(x) - p_n(x) = E_n \quad \text{or} \quad f(x) - p_n(x) = - E_n .$$

(3.4)   *There are always both $\sharp$-points and $\flat$-points.*

This result is intuitively obvious from geometrical considerations. We give a formal proof. The reader is advised to draw diagrams.

Proof. From the general properties of continuous functions there is at least one e-point [cf. (**1.9**)]. Suppose, for instance, that there were no $\sharp$-points. This means that

$$\min\{ p_n(x) - f(x)\} = - E_n + 2 h , \quad E_n \geq h > 0 .$$

Hence

$$E_n \geq p_n(x) - f(x) \geq - E_n + 2h ,$$

which implies

$$E_n - h \geq \big(p_n(x) - h\big) - f(x) \geq - E_n + h ,$$

that is

$$\big| \big(p_n(x) - h\big) - f(x) \big| \leq E_n - h < E_n ,$$

so that $p_n(x)$ is not a polynomial of best approximation, a contradiction.

(3.5_1)   *In the case $n = 1$, there is a sequence of three points in $[a, b]$ which are alternately $\sharp$- and $\flat$-points.*
     This result is also obvious intuitively.

Proof. We now know that there is a $\sharp$-point and a $\flat$-point. We shall show that there must be another e-point in $[a, b]$ and that the signs of the e-points alternate.
     By uniform continuity of $p_1(x) - f(x) = E(x)$, we can divide $[a, b]$ into a set of intervals $I_i = [x_i, x_{i+1}]$ by a set of points x_i with $a = x_0 < x_1 < < \cdots < x_m = b$ with the following property for each $i = 0, 1, 2, \ldots,$ $m - 1$:   *if*

$$x' \in I_i , \quad x'' \in I_i$$

then

$$\big| E(x') - E(x'') \big| < \frac{1}{2} E_1 .$$

Consider any x' in the interval $I_{\sharp}$ in which the $\sharp$-point, say $x_{\sharp}$, lies. Then

$$E(x_{\sharp}) = E_1 \quad \text{and} \quad \big| E(x') - E_1 \big| < \frac{1}{2} E_1 ,$$

so that $E(x') \geq E_1/2 > 0$. Similarly, for x'' in the interval $I_{\flat}$ in which the $\flat$-point lies, we have $E(x'') \leq - E_1/2 < 0$. These two intervals, therefore cannot overlap, or even abut and so we can choose a point z_1 between them. Suppose that the $\sharp$-point is to the left. Then $(z_1 - x)$ has the same sign in the intervals $I_{\sharp}$, $I_{\flat}$ as $E(x)$. Let

$$R = \max_{a \leq x \leq b} \big| z_1 - x \big| .$$

Consider the *'remaining'* intervals I_i. We have, in these, if no other e-point existed,

$$\max \{ \big| E(x) \big| \} < E_1$$

and, there being a finite number of intervals, we have

$$\max_i \{ \max_{x \in I_i} \big| E(x) \big| \} = E^* < E_1 .$$

We observe that $E^* \geq E_1/2$. For the end-points of the intervals $I_\sharp$, $I_\flat$ are also end-points of the 'remaining' intervals and we have seen that the values there satisfy $E(x') \geq E_1/2$, $E(x'') \leq -E_1/2$. Hence certainly $E^* \geq E_1/2$.

We consider, for $\varepsilon > 0$

$$p(x) = p_1(x) - \varepsilon(z_1 - x),$$

which is linear. If we choose ε so small that

$$\varepsilon R < E_1 - E^*,$$

which implies $\varepsilon R < E_1/2$ we see that the deviation of $p(x)$ from $f(x)$ is less than that of $p_1(x)$. For in $I_\sharp$, since $(z_1 - x) > 0$, and in $I_\flat$, since $(z_1 - x) < 0$, and since $\varepsilon R < E_1/2$, the values of $p(x) - f(x)$ have the same signs as those of $p_1(x) - f(x)$, but are reduced in absolute value. In the 'remaining' intervals, the absolute values may be increased, but they cannot exceed

$$E + \varepsilon R < E^* + E_1 - E^* = E_1.$$

Hence p_1 is not a polynomial of best approximation, a contradiction. Thus there must be more than two e-points. These cannot be disposed in the order $\sharp \sharp \flat$ or $\sharp \flat \flat$ by essentially the same argument as above: z_1 is chosen between the $\sharp$-point and the next $\flat$-point. It follows that we must have an alternation $\sharp \flat \sharp$. [We cannot get a similar contradiction in this case because we would have to take a quadratic $(z_1 - x)(z_2 - x)$, which is illegal, to get a perturbation of the correct sign pattern.]

This completes the proof of (3.5_1). We state, without proof, the general result. No essentially new ideas are required in the proof.

(3.5_n) *There is a sequence of $n + 2$ points in $[a, b]$ which are alternately $\sharp$- and $\flat$-points.*

(3.6) *The polynomial of best approximation (of degree $\leq n$) is unique.*

Proof. Suppose there were two, p', p''. We then would have

$$-E_n \leq f - p' \leq E_n,$$

$$-E_n \leq f - p'' \leq E_n.$$

Then $p''' = (p' + p'')/2$ is also a polynomial of best approximation. We can therefore construct, by (3.5), a series of $n + 2$ points, alternately $\sharp$ and $\flat$, for p'''.

Take a $\sharp$-point, $x_\sharp$ for p'''. Then at $x_\sharp$

$$f - p''' = E_n \quad \text{i. e.} \quad (f - p') + (f - p'') = 2 E_n.$$

Since $|p' - f| \leq E_n$, $|p'' - f| \leq E_n$ it follows that $p' - f = p'' - f$. That is p', p'' coincide at any $\sharp$-point. Similarly p', p'' coincide at any $\flat$-point. But there are $n + 2$ e-points. Hence $p' = p''$.

(3.7) $p(x)$ *is the polynomial of best approximation (of degree $\leq n$) to $f(x)$ if there exists a set of $n + 2$ e-points, alternately ♯-points and ♭-points.*

Proof. Suppose

$$\max_{a \leq x \leq b} |f(x) - p(x)| = \mu .$$

Then $\mu \geq E_n$. We shall show that $\mu = E_n$. Suppose not, i.e. $\mu > E_n$. Let $q(x)$ be *the* polynomial of best approximation, and unique by **(3.3)** and **(3.6)**. Then since

$$q(x) - p(x) = q(x) - f(x) + f(x) - p(x)$$

the signs of $q(x) - p(x)$ and $f(x) - p(x)$ coincide at the $n + 2$ e-points of $|f(x) - p(x)|$, because at these points

$$|q - f| \leq E_n , \quad |f - p| = \mu > E_n .$$

Hence the polynomial $q - p$, of degree $\leq n$, has $n + 2$ changes of sign in $[a, b]$ and so $n + 1$ zeros: it therefore vanishes identically. This gives $\mu = \max |f - p| = \max |f - q| = E_n$, in contradiction with our assumption that $\mu > E_n$. Hence $\mu = E_n$.

We can now use this characterization of the polynomial of best approximation to find it explicitly in two simple cases.

$n = 0, f$ *arbitrary.*

If m, M are the minimum and maximum of $f(x)$ in $[a, b]$ it is clear that

$$p_0(x) = \frac{1}{2} (m + M) .$$

$n = 1$ *and f is twice differentiable and convex.*

By the fundamental criterion **(3.7)** $p(x) = A x + B$ is the best approximation if there are three points $x_1 < x_2 < x_3$ in $[a, b]$ for which $f(x) - p(x)$ attains its extreme value alternately. Hence x_2 is definitely inside $[a, b]$ and we can use the differential calculus to conclude that

$$f'(x_2) = A .$$

Now since $f''(x) > 0$, $f'(x)$ is strictly increasing and so $f'(x)$ can only assume the value A once: this means that the derivative of $f - p$ cannot vanish at x_1 or at x_3 and so these extreme points must be end-points: $a = x_1, b = x_3$. Put $x_2 = c$. Then using the equality of the extreme values we must have

$$f(a) - p(a) = f(b) - p(b) = - [f(c) - p(c)]$$

which are equations for A, B which give

$$A = [f(b) - f(a)]/(b - a), \quad B = \frac{1}{2} [f(a) + f(c)] - \frac{1}{2} (a + c) [f(b) - f(a)]/(b - a) .$$

The value of c is given by

$$f'(c) = [f(b) - f(a)]/(b - a) .$$

Remarks

(a) There have recently been intensive studies of the (infinite) algorithms which lead to the polynomials of best approximation. In practice it is found that in many cases very good approximations are found by truncating an expansion in Chebyshev polynomials. This is discussed in detail in the case of $(1 + x)^{-1}$ in $[0, 1]$ in **Problems 3.22/3.23**; in this case the extremal polynomial can be written down. See also RIVLIN (1962). A discussion of $|x|$ in $[-1, 1]$ is given in **Problem 3.28**. Expansions in terms of $T_n(x)$, or $T_n^*(x)$ for various functions are given in **Problems 5.14, 5.16—5.19, 5.25**. For a systematic account of Chebyshev expansions, with tables giving the numerical value of the coefficients, see CLENSHAW (1962).

An interesting heuristic account of the Chebyshev theory, with examples, is given in HASTINGS (1955).

(b) Notice that in the proofs of (**3.3**) . . . (**3.7**) we have not made use of (**3.1**). It is therefore appropriate to outline here an account of (**3.1**), which is more motivated than that given earlier. We use (**3.7**) in the case $f = x^n$, $a = -1, b = 1$, and then we are approximating x^n by polynomials of degree $\leq n - 1$. Then the polynomial $p_{n-1}(x)$ we require is characterized by having

$$y(x) = x^n - p_{n-1}(x) = \pm \mu$$

alternately at $n + 1 = (n - 1) + 2$ points in $[-1, 1]$, where

$$\mu = \max_{-1 \leq x \leq 1} |y(x)| .$$

Now at each interior extrema, at least $n - 1$ in number, we must have $y' = 0$. But y is a polynomial of degree n. Hence all the zeros of y' are simple. Consider

$$f = y^2 - \mu^2 .$$

Since $f' = 2 y y'$ vanishes when $y' = 0$, all the interior extrema of y (and all zeros of y') are double zeros of $y^2 - \mu^2$. Hence $y^2 - \mu^2$ is divisible by y'^2 and the residual factor is a quadratic. This quadratic must be $M(1 - x^2)$ since we must have $|y(\pm 1)| = \mu$. Hence

$$y^2 - \mu^2 = M(1 - x^2) y'^2 ,$$

and if we compare the leading coefficients we find $M = n^{-2}$. If we write $\eta = y/\mu$ we obtain

$$\frac{n \, dx}{\sqrt{1 - x^2}} = \pm \frac{d\eta}{\sqrt{1 - \eta^2}} .$$

Integrating this relation *carefully* we find

$$\eta = \cos (n \arccos x) .$$

(c) The basic ideas in this chapter can be applied in much more general situations. One stage is to the case when we consider weighted approximations to continuous functions by rational functions of assigned degree, where the weight function is an arbitrary positive continuous function. On the other hand, we can consider approximations by families of functions which share with the polynomials the properties we need to draw the conclusion. For some account of this see ACHIESER (1953).

(d) The idea of Chebyshev approximation arises in another important context. Consider the 'solution' of a system of m linear equations in n unknowns, where $m > n$. We can write these as

$$\sum a_{ij} \, x_j + b_i = 0 \, , \quad i = 1, 2, \ldots, m \, .$$

For any assigned set of $\{x_j\}$ we can consider the m residuals

$$\eta_i(x) = \eta_i = \sum a_{ij} \, x_j + b_i \, .$$

We can take for our solution the set of $\{x_j\}$ which minimizes

$$\max_i \left| \, \eta_i(x) \, \right| \, .$$

This is the Chebyshev solution to the system; the 'least squares' solution is that which minimizes

$$\sum \eta_i^2 \, .$$

It is well-known that the 'least-squares' solution can be obtained by solving the corresponding 'normal equations'. It can be shown that the Chebyshev solution can be obtained by an algorithm which is not essentially different from that for solving a system of linear equations by the Gaussian elimination method, or that for solving a 'linear program', in the sense of Dantzig, by the simplex method. See STIEFEL (1959, 1960, 1961) and SCHEID (1961).

Chapter 3. Problems

3.1 Compute $T_n(x)$, $U_n(x)$ for $n = 0(1)\ 6$ where

$$T_0 \equiv 1, \quad T_1 \equiv x, \quad T_n = 2\,x\,T_{n-1} - T_{n-2}, \quad n \geq 2,$$

and

$$U_0 \equiv 1, \quad U_1 \equiv 2\,x, \quad U_n = 2\,x\,U_{n-1} - U_{n-2}, \quad n \geq 2.$$

3.2 Express $\cos n\,\theta$ and

$$\frac{\sin(n+1)\,\theta}{\sin\theta}$$

as polynomials in $\cos\theta$.

3.3 Identify $T_n(x)$ with $\cos(n\arccos x)$ and $U_n(x)$ with

$$\sin((n+1)\arccos x)/\sin(\arccos x).$$

Draw rough graphs of these functions for $n = 0(1)\ 6$.

3.4 Express x^n, for $n = 0(1)\ 6$, as a linear combination of the $T_r(x)$ with $0 \leq r \leq n$. Similarly for $U_n(x)$.

3.5 Evaluate

$$\int_{-1}^{+1} T_m(x)\,T_n(x)\,dx/\sqrt{1-x^2}$$

and

$$\int_{-1}^{+1} U_m(x)\,U_n(x)\,\sqrt{1-x^2}\,dx.$$

3.6 Show that $T_n(x)$ satisfies the differential equation

$$(1 - x^2)\,y'' - x\,y' + n^2\,y = 0.$$

Find a differential equation satisfied by $U_n(x)$.

3.7 Show that between two consecutive zeros of $T_n(x)$ there is exactly one zero of $T_{n-1}(x)$.
  Can $T_n(x)$ and $T_{n-1}(x)$ have a common zero?

3.8 Show that

$$\int_{-1}^{+1} T_n^2(x)\,dx = 1 - (4\,n^2 - 1)^{-1}.$$

3.9 Show $(1 - t\,x)/[1 - 2\,t\,x + t^2]$ is a generating function for $T_n(x)$, i.e. the coefficient of t^n $(n \geq 0)$ in its Maclaurin expansion is $T_n(x)$. Find a similar generating function for $U_n(x)$.

3.10 Find the polynomial of degree n and leading coefficient unity which vanishes at $x = 0$, $x = 1$ and which deviates least from zero in the interval $0 \leq x \leq 1$. [Consider $T_n((2x-1)\cos\pi/2\,n)$.]

3.11 Show that for $n = 1, 2, 3, \ldots$ we have

$$\left| T_n(x) \right| \leq 1, \quad \left| U_n(x) \right| \leq n + 1, \quad -1 \leq x \leq 1.$$

Discuss the equality cases.

3.12 Evaluate

$$\sqrt{2}\left\{ \frac{1}{2} - c\,T_1^*(x) + c^2\,T_2^*(x) - c^3\,T_3^*(x) + \cdots \right\}$$

where

$$T_n^*(x) = T_n(2x-1), \quad c = 3 - 2\sqrt{2}.$$

3.13 Evaluate

$$T_n'(\pm 1).$$

3.14 Find a polynomial $a\,x^2 + b\,x + 1$ which has least deviation from zero in $[-1, 1]$, a, b being arbitrary.

3.15 The same as **Problem 3.14** for $a\,x^2 + x + b$.

3.16 Establish the minimum deviation of $T_2(x)$, using elementary arguments.

3.17 Find the best (1) constant, (2) linear approximation to $1/x$ in the interval $[1, 2]$ for the two norms:

$$M_\infty: \max \left| e(x) \right|,$$

$$M_2: \left\{ \int_1^2 [e(x)]^2 \, dx \right\}^{1/2}.$$

3.18 The same as **Problem 3.17**, for 10^x in $0 \leq x \leq 1$.

3.19 Find the best (1) constant, (2) linear approximation in the Chebyshev sense to $\arctan x$, in $0 \leq x \leq 1$. Draw a rough graph of the error in the linear approximation.

3.20 Let P_k be the class of all polynomials $p(x)$ of degree at most k of the form $p(x) = 1 + x + a_2 x^2 + \cdots + a_k x^k$. For each $p(x)$ there is a greatest $\tau = \tau(p) > 0$ such that $-\tau \leq x \leq 0$ implies $\left| p(x) \right| \leq 1$. Find the polynomial $E_k(x)$ in P_k for which $\tau = \tau_k$ is maximum. What is the value of τ_k? Write down $E_k(x)$ for $k = 2, 3, 4$.

3.21 With the notation of (**1.3**) (1) show that if the x_i $(i = 0, 1, \ldots, n)$ are the zeros of $T_{n+1}(x)$, then

$$l_i(x) = \frac{\dfrac{T_{n+1}(x)}{x - x_i}}{\dfrac{(n+1)(-1)^{i-1}}{\sqrt{1 - x_i^2}}} \; .$$

3.22 Obtain the linear polynomial of best approximation to $(1 + x)^{-1}$ in $[0, 1]$. Compare the result with that given by taking the first two terms of the series in **Problem 3.12** above, i.e.,

$$\sqrt{2}\left[\frac{1}{2} - \left(3 - 2\sqrt{2}\right)(2x - 1)\right] = \frac{1}{2}\left(7\sqrt{2} - 8\right) - \left(6\sqrt{2} - 8\right)x$$

$$= 0.9497 - 0.4853\, x \; .$$

3.23 Show that the polynomial of degree n of best approximation to $(1 + x)^{-1}$ in $[0, 1]$ is, if $c = 3 - 2\sqrt{2}$,

$$\pi_n(x) = \sqrt{2}\left\{\left[\frac{1}{2} - c\, T_1^*(x) + \cdots + (-1)^{n-1} c^{n-1} T_{n-1}^*(x)\right]\right.$$

$$\left. + (-1)^n \frac{c^n}{1 - c^2}\, T_n^*(x)\right\} \; .$$

What is the value of E_n?

Find the corresponding results for $(a + x)^{-1}$, where $a > 0$.

3.24 Deduce from **Problem 3.23** the polynomial of degree $2\,m$ of best approximation to $(1 + x^2)^{-1}$ on $[-1, 1]$.

What is the value of E_{2m+1}?

3.25 Show how to find a quadratic which deviates from x^4 by not more than $9/128$ in $0 \le x \le 1$.

3.26 (TAUSSKY). Given n lines in the same plane, no two of which are parallel, show that among the in-circles in the $\binom{n}{3}$ triangles formed by the lines, there is in general one and only one which cuts or touches the $n - 3$ remaining lines.

Show that there is a point I, whose distances from the lines are not greater than the largest distance of any other point from the lines.

3.27 (GAIER). Let $t_n = t_n(f)$ be the polynomial of degree n of best approximation to f in $[a, b]$ and let p_n be any polynomial of degree n. Then

$$t_n(f - p_n) = t_n(f) - p_n \; .$$

3.28 Let $P_n(x)$ denote the usual Legendre polynomial (see Chapter 5). Obtain the following formal expansions for the interval $[-1, 1]$:

$$|x| = \frac{1}{2} \sum_{n=1}^{\infty} (-1)^{n+1} \frac{(2n-2)!}{(n-1)!\,(n+1)!} \frac{4n+1}{2^{2n}} P_{2n}(x),$$

$$|x| = \frac{2}{\pi} + \frac{4}{\pi} \sum_{n=1}^{\infty} \frac{(-1)^{n+1}}{4n^2-1} T_{2n}(x),$$

$$|x| = \frac{4}{\pi} \sum_{n=0}^{\infty} \frac{(-1)^{n+1}}{(2n-1)(2n+3)} U_{2n}(x).$$

Obtain also the Bernstein polynomials for $|x|$ in this interval.

  By truncation obtain polynomials of degree 0, 2, 4 which approximate $|x|$. Compare the approximation given by these polynomials, in various norms, with that given by the best Chebyshev approximations which have been found by Remez and are

$$\frac{1}{2}, \quad x^2 + \frac{1}{8}, \quad -1.065537\,x^4 + 1.930297\,x^2 + 0.067621.$$

3.29 [Complex analogue of (**3.1**).] If

$$f(z) = a_0 + a_1 z + \cdots + a_n z^n$$

where $a_0, a_1, \ldots,$ are arbitrary complex numbers, show that

$$\max_{|z| \leq 1} |f(z)| \geq |a_0| + |a_n|$$

and there is equality if and only if $f(z) = a_0 + a_n z^n$.

The Theorems of the Markoffs

Let $p_n(x)$ be a polynomial of degree n, such that

$$|p_n(x)| \leq 1, \quad -1 \leq x \leq 1.$$

Does this imply any restriction on the bounds of the derivatives of $p_n(x)$ for $-1 \leq x \leq 1$? This question was raised by the chemist MENDELIEFF for the case of $p_n'(x)$, and was answered by A. A. MARKOFF in 1890.

(4.1) *If $|p_n(x)| \leq 1$ for $-1 \leq x \leq 1$ then $|p_n'(x)| \leq n^2$, $-1 \leq x \leq 1$.* This result is a best possible one: There is equality if and only if

$$p_n(x) = \varepsilon\, T_n(x), \quad |\varepsilon| = 1, x = \pm 1.$$

Repeated applications of **(4.1)** give

(4.2) *If $|p_n(x)| \leq 1$ for $-1 \leq x \leq 1$ then*

$$|p_n^{(k)}(x)| \leq n^2(n-1)^2 \cdots (n-k+1)^2, \quad -1 \leq x \leq 1, \quad k = 1, 2, \ldots, n.$$

This result is not best possible if $k > 1$. The best possible result is the following which is due to W. A. MARKOFF.

(4.3) *If $|p_n(x)| \leq 1$ for $-1 \leq x \leq 1$ then*

$$|p_n^{(k)}(x)| \leq \frac{n^2(n^2 - 1^2) \cdots (n^2 - (k-1)^2)}{1 \cdot 3 \cdots (2k-1)}, \quad -1 \leq x \leq 1, \quad k = 1, 2, \ldots, n.$$

The critical polynomial is again $T_n(x)$. The original proof of this theorem was rather complicated. A simple proof of a somewhat weaker result has been given by ROGOSINSKI (1955). A comparatively simple proof, based on Lagrange interpolation, but using some complex variable ideas has been given by DUFFIN and SCHAEFFER (1941). They show that it is even sufficient to assume $|p_n(x)| \leq 1$ at $x = \cos \nu\, \pi/n$, $\nu = 0, 1, \ldots, n$.

To compare **(4.2)** and **(4.3)** consider $T_4(x)$ for which $T_4''(x) = 96\,x^2 - 16$. The exact bound of $|T_4''(x)|$ is therefore 80 as given by **(4.3)**; the weaker **(4.2)** gives a bound of 144.

We shall now outline a proof of the result of A. A. MARKOFF. We begin with

(4.4) *If $p_{n-1}(x)$ satisfies the inequality*

$$(1 - x^2)^{1/2} |p_{n-1}(x)| \leq 1, \quad -1 \leq x \leq 1, \tag{4.1}$$

then

$$\left| p_{n-1}(x) \right| \le n, \quad -1 \le x \le 1.$$

Proof. We use Lagrangian interpolation at the Chebyshev abscissae. (Compare **Problem 3.21**.) We have, identically

$$p_{n-1}(x) = \sum_{i=1}^{n} \frac{T_n(x)}{x - x_i} \frac{(\sqrt{1 - x_i^2})(-1)^{i-1}}{n} p_{n-1}(x_i).$$

We consider separately the behavior of p_{n-1} in the three sub-intervals

$$[-1, x_n], \quad [x_n, x_1], \quad [x_1, 1].$$

In the middle interval, since $x_1 = -x_n = \cos(\pi/2 n)$, we have

$$(1 - x^2)^{1/2} \ge \sin(\pi/2 n) > (2/\pi)(\pi/2 n) = n^{-1}.$$

Hence, the hypothesis (4.1) implies the conclusion immediately.

The two end-intervals are treated similarly; we deal with $[x_1, 1]$ only. In this interval $T_n(x) = \cos(n \arccos x)$ increases from 0 to 1 and each $x - x_i \ge 0$. Hence, from (4.1),

$$\left| p_{n-1}(x) \right| \le \frac{1}{n} \left| \sum \frac{T_n(x)}{x - x_i} \right| = \frac{1}{n} \left| T_n'(x) \right| = \left| U_{n-1}(x) \right| \le n$$

where we have used **Problem 3.11** at the last step.

The result can be shown to be the best possible: there is equality if and only if $p_{n-1}(x) = r U_{n-1}(x)$, $|r| = 1$, $x = \pm 1$.

A trigonometrical consequence of (**4.4**) is

(4.5) *Let* $s(\phi) = a_1 \sin\phi + \cdots + a_n \sin n\phi$ *satisfy*

$$\left| s(\phi) \right| \le 1, \quad \text{all real } \phi.$$

Then

$$\left| s(\phi)/\sin\phi \right| \le n.$$

Proof. Apply the preceding result to $p_{n-1}(x)$ where $p_{n-1}(\cos\theta) = s(\phi)/\sin\phi$. This result is best possible: there is equality if and only if $s(\phi) \equiv \pm \sin n\phi$. We next establish

(4.6) *If* $t_n(\phi)$ *is a trigonometrical sum of degree* n *and* $\max \left| t_n'(\phi) \right| = 1$ *then* $\max \left| t_n(\phi) \right| \ge n^{-1}$

or, equivalently,

(4.7) *If* $t_n(\theta)$ *is a trigonometrical sum of degree* n *then* $\left| t_n'(\theta) \right| \le n \max \left| t_n(\theta) \right|$.

We shall prove the latter. We may assume $\max \left| t_n(\phi) \right| = 1$. Consider

$$s(\theta, \phi) = \frac{1}{2} \left(t_n(\theta + \phi) - t_n(\theta - \phi) \right).$$

Since

$$\sin(r(\theta + \phi)) - \sin(r(\theta - \phi)) = 2 \cos r\,\theta\, \sin r\,\phi$$

$$\cos(r(\theta + \phi)) - \cos(r(\theta - \phi)) = - 2 \sin r\,\theta\, \sin r\,\phi$$

the hypothesis of (**4.5**) is satisfied by $s(\theta, \phi)$ for any value of the parameter θ. It follows that

$$\left| \frac{s(\theta, \phi)}{\sin\phi} \right| \leq n \ .$$

But

$$\frac{s(\theta, \phi)}{\sin\phi} = \frac{t_n(\theta + \phi) - t_n(\theta - \phi)}{2\,\phi} \frac{\phi}{\sin\phi}$$

and letting $\phi \to 0$, we find

$$\left| t_n'(\theta) \right| \leq n$$

for any fixed θ.

An immediate consequence is the following inequality valid in the interior of $(-1, 1)$.

(**4.8**)   If $p_n(x)$ satisfies $\left| p_n(x) \right| \leq 1$ for $-1 \leq x \leq 1$ then

$$\left| p_n'(x) \right| \leq n/(1 - x^2)^{1/2}, \quad -1 < x < 1 \ .$$

We are now able to deal with the theorem of A. A. MARKOFF. The last inequality can be written as

$$\left| n^{-1}\, p_n'(x)\, (1 - x^2)^{1/2} \right| \leq 1$$

and we can apply (**4.4**) to deduce

$$\left| n^{-1}\, p_n'(x) \right| \leq n \ ,$$

i.e.

$$\left| p_n'(x) \right| \leq n^2 \ .$$

The inequality cases can be traced by going over the argument carefully.

Chapter 4. Problems

4.1 Show that
$$\left| P_n'(x) \right| \le \frac{1}{2}\, n(n+1) , \quad -1 \le x \le 1$$
where $P_n(x)$ is the usual Legendre polynomial. (See Chapter 5.)

4.2 Find a result corresponding to **Problem 4.1** for $U_n'(x)$.

4.3 Deduce from **(4.5)** that
$$\left| a_1 + 2\,a_2 + \cdots + n\,a_n \right| \le n .$$

4.4 (Complex analogue of MARKOFF's Theorem **4.1**). Suppose that $f(z) = b_0 + b_1 z + \cdots + b_n z^n$ satisfies $\left| f(z) \right| \le 1$ for $\left| z \right| \le 1$. Show that
$$\left| f'(z) \right| \le n , \quad \left| z \right| \le 1 .$$

CHAPTER 5

Orthogonal Polynomials

The basic fact is that given any 'reasonable' weight function $w(x)$, non-negative in an interval $[a, b]$ (which may be finite or infinite) and whose integral over any sub-interval of $[a, b]$ is positive, we can construct from the sequence of powers $1, x, x^2, \ldots$ a sequence of polynomials $\pi_n(x)$, of exact degree n, which are normalized and orthogonal with respect to $w(x)$ in $[a, b]$. This is

$$\big(\pi_m(x), \pi_n(x)\big) = \int_a^b \pi_m(x)\, \pi_n(x)\, w(x)\, dx = \delta(m, n) \,. \qquad (5.1)$$

We may assume that the coefficient of x^n in $\pi_n(x)$ is positive. This orthogonalization can be carried out explicitly by the Gram-Schmidt process provided all the moments

$$\mu_n = \int_a^b x^n\, w(x)\, dx \,, \quad n = 0, 1, 2, \ldots, \qquad (5.2)$$

exist and are finite—this is the meaning of the word 'reasonable' in the first line.

The more familiar orthogonal polynomials are those of CHEBYSHEV, LEGENDRE, LAGUERRE, HERMITE and their properties are summarized at the end of this chapter.

We shall give an account of the general properties of orthogonal polynomials. We begin with a proof of the basic result.

Suppose $w(x)$, a real continuous non-negative function defined on an interval (a, b) where $-\infty \le a < b \le \infty$, is such that the moments μ_n defined by (5.2) all exist and are finite. It follows that any scalar product

$$\big(p_m(x), p_n(x)\big) = \int_a^b p_m(x)\, p_n(x)\, w(x)\, dx \,,$$

where $p_m(x)$ and $p_n(x)$ are polynomials exists and is finite. We also suppose that we have

$$\int_c^d w(x)\, dx > 0 \,,$$

when $a \le c < d \le b$.

We proceed to define by induction a sequence of polynomials $\pi_n(x)$, $n = 0, 1, 2, \ldots$ of exact degree n, satisfying (5.1). We begin by writing

$$\pi_0' = 1, \quad \pi_0 = \pi_0'/(\pi_0', \pi_0')^{1/2} .$$

(Observe that it is sometimes convenient to define, conventionally, $\pi_{-1} = 0$.) Assume $\pi_0, \pi_1, \ldots, \pi_n$ defined and satisfying (5.1). We write

$$\pi_{n+1}' = x^{n+1} - \sum_{r=0}^{n} (x^{n+1}, \pi_r)\, \pi_r .$$

It is clear that π_{n+1}' is of exact degree $n + 1$, all the terms in the summation being of degree n at most. Also, if $s \leq n$,

$$(\pi_{n+1}', \pi_s) = (x^{n+1}, \pi_s) - \sum_{r=0}^{n} (x^{n+1}, \pi_r)(\pi_r, \pi_s) = (x^{n+1}, \pi_s) - (x^{n+1}, \pi_s) = 0$$

since, by hypothesis, $(\pi_r, \pi_s) = \delta(r, s)$ for $r, s \leq n$. Hence if we write

$$\pi_{n+1} = \pi_{n+1}'/(\pi_{n+1}', \pi_{n+1}')^{1/2}$$

the sequence $\pi_0, \pi_1, \ldots, \pi_{n+1}$ is normalized and orthogonal. [The division is permissible in view of (5.2).]

This completes an account of the Gram-Schmidt orthogonalization process in a simple context. We shall next show that the orthonormal system we have constructed is the only one.

(5.1)   *The orthonormal system of polynomials associated with $w(x)$ in (a, b) is unique.*

We use the following lemma.

(5.2)   *If $f(x)$ is continuous and non-negative in (a, b) and if*

$$\int_a^b f(x)\, w(x)\, dx = 0$$

then $f(x) \equiv 0$ in $[a, b]$.

Proof of (5.2). If this is false then there is a c, $a \leq c \leq b$ such that $f(c) \neq 0$. Hence, by continuity and non-negativity there is an interval, $[d, e]$, including c, throughout which $f(x) \geq \frac{1}{2} f(c) > 0$. Hence

$$0 = \int_a^b f(x)\, w(x)\, dx \geq \int_d^e f(x)\, w(x)\, dx \geq \frac{1}{2} f(c) \int_d^e w(x)\, dx > 0 ,$$

a contradiction.

Proof of (5.1). We note first that if the $\pi_n(x) = k_n x^n + \cdots$ satisfy (5.1) then since

$$1 = \int_a^b \pi_n^2(x) \, w(x) \, dx = \int_a^b \pi_n(x) \, k_n \, x^n \, w(x) \, dx$$

we have

$$\int_a^b \pi_n(x) \, x^n \, w(x) \, dx = 1/k_n \, .$$

Suppose that

$$\pi_n'(x) = k_n' \, x^n + \cdots , \qquad \pi_n''(x) = k_n'' \, x^n + \cdots$$

both satisfy (5.1). Then

$$\int_a^b \pi_n'(x) \, \pi_n''(x) \, w(x) \, dx = k_n''/k_n' = k_n'/k_n''$$

so that $k_n'' = \pm \, k_n'$. Since both are positive we have $k_n' = k_n''$, and so

$$\int_a^b \pi_n'(x) \, \pi_n''(x) \, w(x) \, dx = 1 \, .$$

We now note that

$$\int_a^b \left(\pi_n'(x) - \pi_n''(x) \right)^2 w(x) \, dx = 1 - 2 + 1 = 0 \, .$$

Hence, by our lemma,

$$\pi_n'(x) = \pi_n''(x) \, .$$

(**5.3**) *All the zeros of $\pi_n(x)$ are real and distinct and lie in the interior of the interval $[a, b]$.*

Proof. Consider the zeros of $\pi_n(x)$. Since all the coefficients are real, complex zeros occur in conjugate pairs, $\alpha \pm i \beta$. The corresponding factors of $\pi_n(x)$ can be combined as $(x - \alpha)^2 + \beta^2$, and this is positive for all x. If there are any (real) zeros of even multiplicity, the corresponding factor $(x - \alpha_r)^{2 n_r}$ is non-negative for all x. The residual, real zeros are of odd multiplicity; denote by $b_1, \ldots, b_k$, those which lie in $[a, b]$. Clearly $k \leq n$, and our result follows if $k = n$.

Observe now that

$$(x - b_1) \, (x - b_2) \cdots (x - b_k) \, \pi_n(x)$$

is of constant sign in $[a, b]$. It follows from (**5.2**) that

$$\int_a^b (x - b_1) \, (x - b_2) \cdots (x - b_k) \, \pi_n(x) \, w(x) \, dx \neq 0 \, .$$

This can only happen if $k = n$, for if $k < n$ the integral vanishes by orthogonality.

(5.4) *Any three consecutive orthogonal polynomials are connected by a linear relation of the form*

$$\pi_{n+1}(x) = (A_n\, x + B_n)\, \pi_n(x) - C_n\, \pi_{n-1}(x)\, , \quad n = 1, 2, \ldots\, .$$

Remark: This relation also holds for $n = 0$, if we interpret $\pi_{-1}(x)$ as being identically zero.

Proof of (5.4). If $\pi_n(x) = k_n\, x^n + k_n'\, x^{n-1} + \cdots$ and if $A_n = k_{n+1}/k_n$ then

$$\pi_{n+1}(x) - A_n\, x\, \pi_n(x) \tag{5.3}$$

is a polynomial of degree at most n which can therefore be expressed as a linear combination of the $\pi_0(x)$, $\pi_1(x)$, ..., $\pi_n(x)$:

$$P_0\, \pi_0(x) + P_1\, \pi_1(x) + \cdots + P_n\, \pi_n(x)\, . \tag{5.4}$$

Using orthogonality we show that $P_0 = P_1 = \cdots = P_{n-2} = 0$ and that

$$- A_n(\pi_n,\, x\, \pi_{n-1}) = P_{n-1}(\pi_{n-1},\, \pi_{n-1}) = P_{n-1}\, .$$

Now since $x\, \pi_{n-1}(x) - k_{n-1}\, \pi_n(x)/k_n$ is a polynomial of degree at most $n - 1$ we have

$$P_{n-1} = - A_n(\pi_n,\, x\, \pi_{n-1}) = - (A_n\, k_{n-1}/k_n)\, (\pi_n,\, \pi_n) = - A_n\, k_{n-1}/k_n\, .$$

If we compare the coefficients of x^n in (5.3) and (5.4) we have

$$k_{n+1}' - A_n\, k_n' = P_n\, k_n\, .$$

We therefore have obtained the required relation:

$$\pi_{n+1} = \left(\frac{k_{n+1}}{k_n}\, x + \frac{k_n\, k_{n+1}' - k_{n+1}\, k_n'}{k_n^2} \right) \pi_n - \frac{k_{n+1}\, k_{n-1}}{k_n^2}\, \pi_{n-1}\, .$$

(5.5) (Interlacing). *If $z_1 < z_2 < \cdots < z_n$ are the zeros of $\pi_n(x)$, and if $Z_1 < Z_2 < \cdots < Z_{n+1}$ are the zeros of $\pi_{n+1}(x)$, then*

$$a < Z_1 < z_1 < Z_2 < z_2 < \cdots < Z_n < z_n < Z_{n+1} < b\, .$$

Proof. We use induction. By **(5.3)**, the zero of $\pi_1(x)$ is inside $[a, b]$. From **(5.4)**, we have

$$\pi_2(z_1) = - k_2\, k_0\, \pi_0/k_1^2 < 0\, .$$

Now $\pi_2(z)$ is a quadratic with positive leading coefficient. Hence $\pi_2(z)$ has two real zeros, separated by z_1 and, by **(5.3)**, lying inside $[a, b]$. This establishes **(5.5)** in the case $n = 1$.

Now suppose that our theorem has been established for π_{n-1} and π_n so that we have

$$a < z_1 < y_1 < z_2 < \cdots < y_{n-1} < z_n < b$$

where $y_1, \ldots, y_{n-1}$ are the zeros of π_{n-1}. Since $\pi_n(z_r) = 0$, $\pi_n(z_{r+1}) = 0$ we have

$$\pi_{n+1}(z_r) = -\, k_{n+1}\, k_{n-1}\, \pi_{n-1}(z_r)/k_n^2 \,,$$

$$\pi_{n+1}(z_{r+1}) = -\, k_{n+1}\, k_{n-1}\, \pi_{n-1}(z_{r+1})/k_n^2 \,.$$

But by our inductive hypothesis there is exactly one zero, y_r, of π_{n-1} between z_r, z_{r+1} and therefore also π_{n+1} have opposite signs at z_r, z_{r+1}. This locates $n - 1$ zeros of π_{n+1}. We have to show that there are further zeros between a and z_1 and between z_n and b. Since the leading coefficients of the π_n are assumed positive, π_{n+1} and π_{n-1} have the same sign for $|x|$ large. But they have opposite signs at z_1, z_n. But π_{n-1} does not change sign to the left of z_1 or to the right of z_n; hence π_{n+1} must do so. Thus there are zeros of π_{n+1} to the left of z_1 and to the right of z_n—by (**5.3**) these must be inside (a, b). This is all we require.

We now want to discuss some extremal properties of orthogonal expansions. It is convenient to discuss this in a somewhat general setting[1](cf. Chapter 8 below). Suppose given a set (or space) of functions provided with an inner product $(,)$. Two functions f, g of this space are said to be *orthogonal* if $(f, g) = 0$. A sequence of functions $\{\phi_n\}$ is said to be an *orthogonal system* (*O.S.*) if $(\phi_n, \phi_m) = 0$, $n \neq m$; it is said to be a normal *O.S.* if, in addition, $(\phi_n, \phi_n) = 1$. Given such a *N.O.S.* we can ask whether it is possible to represent an arbitrary function f as a linear combination of the ϕ_n:

$$f = \sum a_n \phi_n \,. \tag{5.5}$$

Proceeding formally, on this assumption, it is easy to calculate the a_n. Indeed

$$(f, \phi_n) = \left(\sum a_r \phi_r, \phi_n\right) = \sum a_r(\phi_r, \phi_n) = \sum a_r \, \delta(r, n) = a_n \,.$$

These a_n are called the *Fourier coefficients* of f with respect to $\{\phi_n\}$. The fact that we can calculate the Fourier coefficients in a special case gives us no guarantee about the truth of (5.5). (See e.g. **Problem 5.3**).

It is clear that if there were non-trivial functions f such that

$$(f, \phi_n) \equiv 0, \quad n = 0, 1, 2, \ldots,$$

then different functions could have the same Fourier coefficients. We call a sequence $\{\phi_n\}$ *complete* if this cannot happen. For instance the sequence

---

[1] A natural setting for this theory is the space L^2. It is not our purpose here to develop the appropriate theory rigorously and our treatment is formal.

$\sin x$, $\sin 2\, x$, ... is not complete in $(0, 2\,\pi)$ for all the Fourier coefficients of $\cos x$ with respect to this sequence vanish. (It is, however, complete in $(0, \pi)$).

The *formal* series $\sum a_r \phi_r$ is called the *Fourier series* of f with respect to $\{\phi_n\}$. The partial sums,

$$ f_n = \sum_{r=0}^{n} a_r \phi_r , $$

of this are called the *Fourier polynomials* of f with respect to $\{\phi_n\}$; we call *any* finite sum

$$ \sum_{r=0}^{n} c_r \phi_r $$

a 'trigonometrical polynomial' of degree n.

(5.6) *Among all the trigonometrical polynomials of degree n, that which gives the best mean-square approximation to $f(x)$ is the Fourier polynomial.*

Proof. We want to minimize, with respect to the c_r,

$$ \int_a^b \left[f(x) - \sum_{r=0}^{n} c_r \, \phi_r(x) \right]^2 dx . $$

(We have taken a simple, weightless case!) We have

$$ \int_a^b \left[f(x) - \sum_{r=0}^{n} c_r \, \phi_r(x) \right]^2 dx $$

$$ = \int_a^b f^2(x) \, dx - 2 \sum c_r \int_a^b f(x)\,\phi_r(x) \, dx + \sum_{r,\,s=0}^{n} c_r\, c_s \int_a^b \phi_r(x)\, \phi_s(x) \, dx $$

$$ = \int_a^b f^2(x) \, dx - 2 \sum a_r\, c_r + \sum c_r^2 $$

$$ = \int_a^b f^2(x) \, dx + \sum (c_r - a_r)^2 - \sum a_r^2 . $$

The right hand side is not less than

$$ \int_a^b f^2(x) \, dx - \sum_{r=0}^{n} a_r^2 = \int_a^b \left[f(x) - \sum_{r=0}^{n} a_r\, \phi_r(x) \right]^2 dx $$

no matter what the c_r are, and there is equality if and only if $c_r = a_r$. This is the result required. The same argument applies in the general context to show that the Fourier polynomial is the best polynomial approximation in the sense of the norm induced by the inner product.

(5.7) *Among all polynomials $\tilde{p}_n(x)$ of degree n and leading coefficient unity, that which minimizes*

$$\int_a^b \tilde{p}_n(x)^2\, w(x)\, dx$$

is $\tilde{\pi}_n(x)$, where the $\{\pi_n(x)\}$ are orthogonal with respect to $w(x)$ over $[a, b]$.

Proof. We can write

$$\tilde{p}_n(x) = \tilde{\pi}_n(x) + \sum_{r=0}^{n-1} \alpha_r\, \tilde{\pi}_r(x) .$$

Hence

$$\int_a^b \tilde{p}_n^2(x)\, w(x)\, dx = \int_a^b \tilde{\pi}_n^2(x)\, w(x)\, dx + 2\sum_{r=0}^{n-1} \alpha_r \int_a^b \tilde{\pi}_n(x)\, \tilde{\pi}_r(x)\, w(x)\, dx$$

$$+ \sum_{r,\, s=0}^{n-1} \alpha_r\, \alpha_s \int_a^b \tilde{\pi}_r(x)\, \tilde{\pi}_s(x)\, w(x)\, dx$$

$$= \int_a^b \tilde{\pi}_n^2(x)\, w(x)\, dx + \sum_{r=0}^{n-1} (\alpha_r/k_r)^2 .$$

In words, (**5.7**) says that $\tilde{\pi}_n(x)$ is the best mean square approximation to zero, by polynomials of degree n and leading coefficient unity.

We shall now discuss a little further the concept of completeness introduced earlier.

(5.8) *If the range $[a, b]$ is finite the corresponding sequence $\{\pi_n(x)\}$ is complete (for continuous functions).*

Proof. Suppose $f(x)$ is continuous in $[a, b]$. Take any $\varepsilon > 0$. Then by WEIERSTRASS' Theorem (**2.1**) there is a polynomial $p(x) = p_\varepsilon(x)$ such that

$$|f(x) - p(x)| < \varepsilon, \quad a \leq x \leq b .$$

Now if we take n larger than the degree of $p_\varepsilon(x)$, by (**5.6**)

$$\int_a^b [f(x) - f_n(x)]^2\, w(x)\, dx \leq \int_a^b [f(x) - p(x)]^2\, w(x)\, dx$$

and so

$$\int_a^b [f(x) - f_n(x)]^2\, w(x)\, dx = \int_a^b f^2(x)\, w(x)\, dx - \sum_{r=0}^n a_r^2 < \mu_0\, \varepsilon^2 .$$

Hence

$$0 \leq \int_a^b f^2(x)\, w(x)\, dx - \sum_{r=0}^{\infty} a_r^2 < \mu_0\, \varepsilon^2 .$$

This means, ε being arbitrary, that

$$\int_a^b f^2(x)\, w(x)\, dx = \sum_{r=0}^{\infty} a_r^2 . \tag{5.6}$$

To show that $\{\pi_n(x)\}$ is complete for continuous functions we have to show that if all the $F.C.$ of any continuous $f(x)$ vanish, then so does f. But this is now evident from (5.6) and the basic lemma.

The equality (5.6) is usually known as PARSEVAL's Theorem.

(5.9) (Finite Moment Theorem). *If $f(x)$ is continuous in a finite interval $[a, b]$ and if all its moments*

$$\mu_n = \int_a^b x^n f(x)\, w(x)\, dx = 0 , \quad n = 0, 1, 2, \ldots$$

then $f(x)$ is identically zero.

This is equivalent to **(5.8)**. It is important to note that we cannot extend this to an infinite interval. This is shown, e.g., by the following example due to T. J. STIELTJES:

$$f(x) = \exp(-x^{1/4}) \sin x^{1/4} , \quad w(x) \equiv 1 .$$

For this function we have, if $\mathscr{I}()$ denotes imaginary part of ( ):

$$\mu_n = \int_0^{\infty} x^n \exp(-x^{1/4}) \sin x^{1/4} \, dx$$

$$= 4 \int_0^{\infty} e^{-y}\, y^{4n+3} \sin y \, dy$$

$$= 4\, \mathscr{I} \int_0^{\infty} \exp(-(1-i)\, y)\, y^{4n+3} \, dy$$

$$= 4\, \mathscr{I} \left[(1-i)^{-4n-4} \int_0^{\infty} e^{-y}\, y^{4n+3} \, dy \right]$$

$$= 4\, \mathscr{I} \left[(-4)^{-n-1}\, \Gamma(4n+4) \right]$$

$$= 0 .$$

Chebyshev Polynomials $T_n(x)$

$$T_n(x) = \cos(n \arccos x) = x^n - \binom{n}{2} x^{n-2} (1 - x^2) + \binom{n}{4} x^{n-4} (1 - x^2)^2 - \cdots$$

$$= \frac{n}{2} \sum_{m=0}^{[n/2]} \frac{(-1)^m (n - m - 1)!}{m! (n - 2m)!} (2x)^{n-2m}$$

$$= 2^{n-1} \left[x^n - \frac{n}{4} x^{n-2} + \cdots \right]$$

$$T_0 = 1, \quad T_1 = x, \quad T_2 = 2x^2 - 1, \, T_3 = 4x^3 - 3x, \quad T_4 = 8x^4 - 8x^2 + 1, \ldots .$$

Recurrence Relation

$$T_{n+1} - 2x T_n + T_{n-1} = 0, \quad T_0 = 1, T_1 = x .$$

$$(1 - x^2) T_n' = n T_{n-1} - n x T_n .$$

Differential Equation

$$(1 - x^2) y'' - x y' + n^2 y = 0 .$$

Generating Function

$$\frac{1 - t x}{1 - 2 t x + t^2} = \sum_{n=0}^{\infty} T_n(x) t^n .$$

Orthogonality

$$\int_{-1}^{+1} T_m(x) T_n(x) \, dx / \sqrt{1 - x^2} = \begin{cases} 0, & m \neq n \\ \pi, & m = n = 0 \\ \pi/2, & m = n > 0 . \end{cases}$$

'Rodrigues' Formula

$$T_n(x) = \{ (-1)^n (1 - x^2)^{1/2} / (2n - 1)!! \} D^n (1 - x^2)^{n - 1/2} .$$

Bounds

$$| T_n(x) | \leq 1, \quad -1 \leq x \leq 1 .$$

Approximate Quadrature (cf. Chapter 9)

Nodes and Christoffel Numbers: $\cos((2k - 1) \pi/2n)$, π/n, $k = 1, 2, \ldots, n$.
Coefficient of $f^{(2n)}(\zeta)$ in error estimate: $\pi / \{ 2^{2n-1} (2n)! \}$.

Chebyshev Polynomials $U_n(x)$

$$U_n(x) = \frac{1}{n+1} T'_{n+1}(x) = \frac{\sin\{(n+1)\arccos x\}}{\sin\{\arccos x\}}$$

$$= \binom{n+1}{1} x^n - \binom{n+1}{3} x^{n-2}(1-x^2) + \binom{n+1}{5} x^{n-4}(1-x^2)^3 - \cdots$$

$$= \sum_{m=0}^{[n/2]} \frac{(-1)^m (n-m)!}{m!\,(n-2m)!} (2x)^{n-2m}$$

$$= 2^n \left[x^n - \frac{n-1}{4} x^{n-2} + \cdots \right]$$

$$U_0 = 1, \quad U_1 = 2x, \quad U_2 = 4x^2 - 1, \quad U_3 = 8x^3 - 4x,$$

$$U_4 = 16x^4 - 12x^2 + 1, \cdots.$$

Recurrence Relation

$$U_{n+1} - 2xU_n + U_{n-1} = 0, \quad U_0 = 1, \ U_1 = 2x.$$

$$(1-x^2) U'_n = (n+1) U_{n-1} - nxU_n.$$

Differential Equation

$$(1-x^2) y'' - 3xy' + n(n+2) y = 0.$$

Generating Function

$$\frac{1}{1-2xt+t^2} = \sum_{n=0}^{\infty} U_n(x) t^n.$$

Orthogonality

$$\int_{-1}^{+1} U_m(x) U_n(x) (1-x^2)^{1/2}\,dx = \begin{cases} 0, & m \neq n \\ \pi/2, & m = n \end{cases}.$$

'Rodrigues' Formula

$$U_n(x) = [(-1)^n (1-x^2)^{-1/2}/(2n+1)!!] D^n \{(1-x^2)^{n+1/2}\}.$$

Bounds

$$|U_n(x)| \leq n+1, \quad -1 \leq x \leq 1.$$

Approximate Quadrature (cf. Chapter 9)

Nodes and Christoffel Numbers:

$$\cos(k\pi/(n+1)), \ [\pi \sin^2(k\pi/(n+1))]/(n+1), \quad k = 1, 2, \ldots, n.$$

Coefficients of $f^{(2n)}(\zeta)$ in error estimate: $\pi/[(2n)!\,2^{2n+1}]$.

Legendre Polynomials

$$P_n(x) = \frac{(2\,n)\,!}{2^n(n\,!)^2}\left[x^n - \frac{n(n-1)}{2(2\,n-1)}\,x^{n-2} + \frac{n(n-1)\,(n-2)(n-3)}{2\times 4\,(2\,n-1)\,2\,n-3)}\,x^{n-4} - \cdots\right]$$

$$P_0 = 1, \quad P_1 = x, \quad P_2 = \frac{3}{2}\,x^2 - \frac{1}{2}, \quad P_3 = \frac{5}{2}\,x^3 - \frac{3}{2}\,x,$$

$$P_4 = \frac{35}{8}\,x^4 - \frac{15}{4}\,x^2 + \frac{3}{8}, \ldots.$$

Recurrence Relation

$$(n+1)\,P_{n+1} - (2\,n+1)\,x\,P_n + n\,P_{n-1} = 0, \quad P_0 = 1, P_1 = x.$$

$$(x^2-1)\,P_n' = n\,x\,P_n - n\,P_{n-1} = (n+1)\,P_{n+1} - (n+1)\,x\,P_n.$$

Differential Equation

$$(1 - x^2)\,y'' - 2\,x\,y' + n(n+1)\,y = 0.$$

Generating Function

$$\frac{1}{\sqrt{1 - 2\,t\,x + t^2}} = \sum_{n=0}^{\infty} P_n(x)\,t^n.$$

Orthogonality

$$\int_{-1}^{+1} P_m(x)\,P_n(x)\,dx = \begin{cases} 0, & m \neq n \\ \left(n + \frac{1}{2}\right)^{-1}, & m = n. \end{cases}$$

'Rodrigues' Formula

$$P_n(x) = \left[1/(2^n(n\,!))\right] D^n\{(x^2 - 1)^n\}.$$

Bounds

$$\left|P_n(x)\right| \leq 1, \quad -1 \leq x \leq 1.$$

Approximate Quadrature (cf. Chapter 9)

Nodes and Christoffel Numbers: Lowan, Davids and Levenson (1942). Coefficient of $f^{(2n)}(\zeta)$ in error estimate: $2^{2n+1}(n!)^4/\{[(2\,n)\,!]^3\,(2\,n+1)\}$.

Laguerre Polynomials

$$L_n(x) = (-1)^n \left[x^n - \frac{n^2}{1} x^{n-1} + \frac{n^2 (n-1)^2}{1 \times 2} x^{n-2} - \cdots + (-1)^n n! \right]/n!$$

$$L_0 = 1, \quad L_1 = 1 - x, \quad L_2 = 1 - 2x + \frac{1}{2} x^2,$$

$$L_3 = 1 - 3x + \frac{3}{2} x^2 - \frac{1}{6} x^3, \ldots .$$

[Note: Here we have sign $k_n = (-1)^n$, contrary to our usual convention.]

Recurrence Relation

$$(n+1) L_{n+1} - (2n+1-x) L_n + n L_{n-1} = 0, \quad L_0 = 1, L_2 = 1 - x.$$

$$x L_n' = n L_n - n L_{n-1} = (n+1) L_{n+1} - (n+1-x) L_n.$$

Differential Equation
$$x y'' + (1-x) y' + n y = 0.$$

Generating Function
$$\frac{1}{1-t} \exp\left[\frac{-xt}{1-t}\right] = \sum_{n=0}^{\infty} L_n(x) t^n.$$

Orthogonality
$$\int_0^{\infty} L_m(x) L_n(x) e^{-x} dx = \begin{cases} 0, m \neq n \\ 1, m = n \end{cases}.$$

'Rodrigues' Formula
$$L_n(x) = \{e^x/n!\} D^n (e^{-x} x^n).$$

Bounds

If
$$\phi_n(x) = e^{-x/2} L_n(x),$$

then
$$|\phi_n(x)| \leq 1.$$

Approximate Quadrature (cf. Chapter 9)

Nodes and Christoffel numbers: SALZER and ZUCKER (1949).
Coefficient of $f^{(2n)}(\zeta)$ in error estimate: $(n!)^2/(2n)!$.

Hermite Polynomials

$$H_n(x) = (2\,x)^n - \frac{n(n-1)}{1!}\,(2\,x)^{n-2} + \frac{n(n-1)\,(n-2)\,(n-3)}{2!}\,(2\,x)^{n-4} - \cdots$$

$$H_0 = 1, \quad H_1 = 2\,x, \quad H_2 = 4\,x^2 - 2, \quad H_3 = 8\,x^3 - 12\,x,$$

$$H_4 = 16\,x^4 - 48\,x^2 + 12, \ldots .$$

(Remark: Various other normalizations are in use.)

Recurrence Relation

$$H_{n+1} - 2\,x\,H_n + 2\,n\,H_{n-1} = 0\,, \quad H_0 = 1, H_1 = 2\,x\,.$$

$$H_n' = 2\,n\,H_{n-1}\,.$$

Differential Equation

$$y'' - 2\,x\,y' + 2\,n\,y = 0\,.$$

Generating Function

$$\exp\left(-\,t^2 + 2\,x\,t\right) = \sum_{n=0}^{\infty} H_n(x)\,t^n/n!\,.$$

Orthogonality

$$\int_{-\infty}^{+\infty} H_m(x)\,H_n(x)\,e^{-x^2}\,dx = \begin{cases} 0, \ m \neq n \\ 2^n \times n!\,\sqrt{\pi}, \ m = n \end{cases}.$$

'Rodrigues' Formula

$$H_n(x) = \left[(-1)^n\,e^{x^2}\right] D^n\left\{\left(e^{-x^2}\right)\right\}\,.$$

Bounds

If

$$\phi_n(x) = \left(\sqrt{\pi}\,\,2^n\,n!\right)^{-1/2} e^{-x^2/2}\,H_n(x)$$

then

$$\left|\phi_n(x)\right| \leq \phi_0(0) = \pi^{-1/4}\,.$$

Approximate Quadrature (cf. Chapter 9)

Nodes and Christoffel numbers: SALZER, ZUCKER and CAPUANO (1952). Coefficient of $f^{(2n)}(\zeta)$ in error estimate: $\sqrt{\pi}(n!)/(2\,n)!\,2^n$.

Jacobi Polynomials

These are the polynomials orthogonal in $[-1, 1]$ with respect to the weight function $w(x) = (1 - x)^\alpha (1 + x)^\beta$ where $\alpha > -1$, $\beta > -1$. The ultraspherical polynomials correspond to the case $\alpha = \beta$. Various normalizations are in use. If the basic interval is taken to be $[0, 1]$ the polynomials orthogonal with respect to $x^{q-1}(1 - x)^{p-q}$ are denoted by $\{G_n(p, q, x)\}$; these have been tabulated by KARMAZINA (1954).

Bibliography

There is an enormous literature dealing with orthogonal polynomials. The standard treatise is SZEGÖ (1959). A summary of the theory is available in ERDÉLYI (1953) or in MAGNUS and OBERHETTINGER (1948). See also SANSONE (1959).

Tables and graphs of the polynomials are available as follows:

CHEBYSHEV: NATIONAL BUREAU OF STANDARDS (1952), JONES et al. (1946), JAHNKE-EMDE-LÖSCH (1960).
LEGENDRE: JAHNKE-EMDE-LÖSCH (1960), BRITISH ASSOCIATION MATHEMATICAL TABLES (1946).
LAGUERRE: SLATER (1955), WIENER (1949).
JACOBI: KARMAZINA (1956).

Collections of tables of zeros of these (and other orthogonal) polynomials and the corresponding Christoffel numbers are available in KOPAL (1962), LANCZOS (1955), NATIONAL BUREAU OF STANDARDS (1954), SALZER, ZUCKER and CAPUANO (1952). The generalized Laguerre case, in which $a = 0$, $b = \infty$, $w(x) = x^\alpha e^{-x}$, $\alpha > -1$ has been discussed by RABINOWITZ and WEISS (1959). (Cf. **Problem 5.6.**) There have been some recent tables of these quantities for polynomials of high order, up to 96. We mention, in particular, those of DAVIS and RABINOWITZ (1956, 1958).

A comprehensive set of formulas, tables and graphs for orthogonal polynomials is contained in HOCHSTRASSER (1963).

For tables and graphs of the corresponding orthogonal *functions*, i. e., $\pi_n(x) \sqrt{w(x)}$, see, in particular, JAHNKE-EMDE-LÖSCH (1960).

Chapter 5. Problems

5.1   Find the Fourier coefficients of the periodic function equal to x in the interval $[-\pi, \pi)$:

$$a_n = \frac{1}{\pi} \int\limits_{-\pi}^{\pi} x \cos n x \, dx, \qquad b_n = \frac{1}{\pi} \int\limits_{-\pi}^{+\pi} x \sin n x \, dx \, .$$

5.2   Find the Fourier coefficients of the functions $|\sin x|$ and $|\cos x|$.

5.3   If $f(x) = (\pi - x)/2$, $0 \le x < 2\pi$, and has period 2π, find the Fourier series for $f(x)$: $\sum b_k \sin k x$. Does this series represent the function at $x = 0$?

5.4   If $f(x)$ is differentiable and has period 1 is it necessary for $f'(x)$ and $\int\limits_{0}^{x} f(t) \, dt$ to have period 1? If not, indicate simple conditions sufficient to ensure periodicity.

5.5   Expand $|x|$ in a series of Legendre Polynomials

$$|x| \sim a_0 P_0(x) + a_1 P_1(x) + a_2 P_2(x) + \cdots .$$

(Compare **Problem 3.28.**)

5.6   Let m be a fixed positive integer.
(i)   Evaluate

$$\mu_n = \int\limits_{0}^{\infty} x^{m+n} e^{-x} \, dx \, .$$

(ii)   Show that for any c, d, $0 \le c < d \le \infty$ we have

$$\int\limits_{c}^{d} x^m e^{-x} \, dx > 0 \, .$$

(iii)   Show that
$$L_n^{(m)}(x) = (e^x x^{-m}/n!) \, D^n [e^{-x} x^{m+n}]$$

is a polynomial of degree n and find the coefficients k_n, k_n' of x^n and x^{n-1}.

(iv)   Show that the $L_n^{(m)}(x)$, $n = 0, 1, 2, \ldots$, form an orthogonal system of polynomials, with respect to the weight function $x^m e^{-x}$, in the interval $[0, \infty)$.

(v)   Find an expression for the corresponding normalized orthogonal polynomials and evaluate it for $n = 0, 1, 2, 3$.

5.7   Show that $|P_n(x)| \le 1$ for $-1 \le x \le 1$.

5.8   Prove that the derivatives of the classical orthogonal polynomials are themselves orthogonal.

5.9   Evaluate

$$\sum_{k=1}^{n} (-1)^k \cos \frac{k\, m\, \pi}{n+1}\,.$$

5.10   Evaluate

$$\frac{1}{r+1} \sum_{k=0}^{n} (-1)^{k+1} \left[\cos^{r+1}(k+1)\,\theta - \cos^{r+1} k\,\theta\right]$$

where $\theta = \pi/(n+1)$.

5.11   We have seen that among the polynomials $\tilde{p}_n(x) = x^n + \cdots$ that which is the best approximation to zero in the Chebyshev sense is $\tilde{T}_n(x)$ and that which is the best approximation to zero in the mean-square sense is $\tilde{P}_n(x)$. Compare, for general, and for large n, the efficiencies of $\tilde{P}_n(x)$ and $\tilde{T}_n(x)$, as approximations to zero, in both norms.

5.12   Suppose $\{\pi_n(x)\}$ are the polynomials orthogonal with respect to $w(x)$ in the interval $[a, b]$ and write

$$l_i(x) = \pi_n(x)/\pi'_n(x_i)\,(x - x_i)\,.$$

(i)   Prove that l_i and l_j are orthogonal with respect to $w(x)$ in $[a, b]$.
(ii)   Prove that

$$\sum_{i=1}^{n} \int_a^b w(x)\,[l_i(x)]^2\,dx = \int_a^b w(x)\,dx\,.$$

5.13   (CHRISTOFFEL-DARBOUX). Use **(5.4)** to show that if $x \neq y$

$$\sum_{r=0}^{n} \pi_r(x)\,\pi_r(y) = \frac{k_n}{k_{n+1}} \times \frac{\pi_{n+1}(x)\,\pi_n(y) - \pi_n(x)\,\pi_{n+1}(y)}{x - y}\,.$$

Discuss the case when $x = y$.

5.14   Expand $|x|$ in a series of Chebyshev polynomials of the first kind in $[-1, 1]$. Also expand in a series of Chebyshev polynomials of the second kind.

5.15   Compare the errors, in the maximum and the root mean square norms, committed by truncating the expansions given in **Problems 5.14** and **5.5** at various stages.

5.16   Expand $\arctan x$ in a series of Chebyshev polynomials of the first kind in $[-1, 1]$.

5.17   The same as **Problem 5.16** for $\cos\frac{1}{4}\pi x$, $\cos\frac{1}{2}\pi x$.

5.18   The same as **Problem 5.16** for $\log_e[(a + x)/(a - x)]$, where $a > 1$.

5.19 Expand $\log_e(1 + x)$ in a series of Chebyshev polynomials of the first kind in $[0, 1]$.

5.20 Show that the Jacobi polynomials

$$P_n^{(\alpha,\,\beta)}(x) = \frac{(-1)^n}{2^n\, n!}\, (1 - x)^{-\alpha}(1 + x)^{-\beta} \left(\frac{d}{dx}\right)^n \left\{(1 - x)^{n+\alpha}\, (1 - x)^{n+\beta}\right\}$$

are orthogonal with respect to the weight function

$$(1 - x)^\alpha\, (1 + x)^\beta, \quad \alpha > -1, \beta > -1,$$

on the interval $[-1, 1]$.

5.21 (i) Estimate the error term in the expansion of $(1 - t)^{1/2}$ by carrying out the differentiation and then approximating by STIRLING's Formula (7.25).

(ii) [BURKILL (1959)]. Consider the Bernstein polynomials for $|y|$ in $[-1, 1]$, i.e.,

$$B_n(y) = \sum_{k=0}^{n} \left|\frac{2k - n}{n}\right| \binom{n}{k} \left(\frac{1 + y}{2}\right)^k \left(\frac{1 - y}{2}\right)^{n-k}.$$

Estimate $B_n(0)$.

5.22 Show that the polynomials $\pi_n(x)$ obtained by orthonormalization of $1, x, x^2, \ldots$ with respect to a real inner product $(,)$ can be defined by

$$\pi'_{-1} = 0, \quad \pi'_0 = 1,$$

$$\pi'_{n+1} = x\, \pi_n - (x\, \pi_n, \pi_n)\, \pi_n - \sqrt{(\pi'_n, \pi'_n)}\, \pi_{n-1},$$

$$\pi_n = \pi'_n / \sqrt{(\pi'_n, \pi'_n)}.$$

(Primes do *not* denote differentiation here.)

5.23 Retaining the notation of the previous example, show that the coefficients a_{nj} in $\pi_n(x)$:

$$\pi_n(x) = a_{n0} + a_{n1} x + \cdots + a_{nn} x^n, \quad n = 0, 1, \ldots,$$

can be calculated by the following recurrence relations:

$$a_{00} = 1 / \sqrt{(\pi'_0, \pi'_0)}; \quad a_{i,j} = 0, \quad j > i;$$

$$a_{n+1,j} = [a_{n,j-1} - (x\, \pi_n, \pi_n)\, a_{n,j} - \sqrt{(\pi'_n, \pi'_n)}\, a_{n-1,j}] / \sqrt{(\pi'_{n+1}, \pi'_{n+1})},$$

$$n = 0, 1, \ldots, \quad j = 0, 1, \ldots, n + 1.$$

CHAPTER 6

Interpolation and Interpolation Processes

Interpolation is reading between the lines of tables. Linear (or 2-point) interpolation is accomplished by assuming the function tabulated is linear between the points of tabulation. If $a + h = b$, $0 \leq p \leq 1$, we then take:

$$f(a + p\,h) \doteq f(a) + p\,[f(b) - f(a)] = (1 - p)\,f(a) + p\,f(b)\ .$$

We cannot possibly estimate the error unless we know something about the behavior of $f(x)$ in the interval $[a, b]$. We are likely to be in trouble if $f'(x)$ does not exist. A convenient assumption is that $f''(x)$ is bounded, by M, say, in $[a, b]$. With this we have, by TAYLOR's Theorem, for some $c = c(p)$:

$$f(a + p\,h) = f(a) + p\,h\,f'(a) + \frac{p^2\,h^2}{2!}\,f''(c)\ ,\quad a \leq c \leq b\,;$$

$$f(b) = f(a) + h\,f'(a) + \frac{h^2}{2!}\,f''(d)\ ,\quad a \leq d \leq b\ .$$

Hence

$$f(a + p\,h) - f(a) - p[f(b) - f(a)] = \frac{1}{2}\,h^2\,[p^2\,f''(c) - p\,f''(d)]\ .$$

If we are more careful we can obtain this result with $c = d = \zeta$, $a \leq \zeta \leq b$. Indeed consider

$$F(p) = f(a + p\,h) - f(a) - p[f(b) - f(a)] - K\,p(p - 1)$$

and choose K so that $F(p_0) = 0$ for some $p_0 \neq 0$, $\neq 1$. Then $F(p)$ has three zeros in $[0, 1]$: 0, 1, p_0. Hence $F''(\theta) = 0$, for some θ, $0 \leq \theta \leq 1$. That is

$$h^2\,f''(a + \theta\,h) = 2\,K\ .$$

Hence substituting

$$f(a + p_0\,h) = f(a) + p_0\,[f(b) - f(a)] + \frac{h^2\,(p_0^2 - p_0)}{2}\,f''(\zeta)$$

where $\zeta = a + \theta\,h$ depends on p_0. We can now drop the subscript and have

$$f(a + p\,h) = f(a) + p\,[f(b) - f(a)] + \frac{h^2\,(p^2 - p)}{2}\,f''(\zeta)\ .$$

This gives

$$\left| f(a + p\,h) - f(a) - p\,[f(b) - f(a)] \right| \leq \frac{1}{2}\,h^2 \times M\,p(1 - p) \leq \frac{1}{8} \times h^2\,M\ . \tag{6.1}$$

(With this estimate it is easy to see how much error is possible if we interpolate linearly in a given table, assuming the entries in it to be correct. E.g. in a table of $\sin x$, the error when the interval is 0.02, is at most $10^{-4}/2$ so that linear interpolation would be appropriate for a $4\,D$ table.)

In general linear interpolation is not adequate and we must consider higher order interpolation. Whereas in manual work, using tables, it is more convenient to use tables at equal intervals and interpolation formulae using (central) differences (e.g. EVERETT's), in automatic computation, unequal intervals cause little if any trouble and Lagrangian Interpolation is more usual. Tables to facilitate the use of the Lagrangian method in the equal interval case are available. If we use the 4-point case then

$$f(p) = L_{-1}(p)\, f(-1) + L_0(p)\, f(0) + L_1(p)\, f(1) + L_2(p)\, f(2)$$

where

$$L_{-1}(p) = -\frac{1}{6}\, p(p-1)\,(p-2)\,, \quad L_0(p) = \frac{1}{2}\,(p+1)\,(p-1)\,(p-2)\,,$$

$$L_1(p) = -\frac{1}{2}\,(p+1)\,p(p-2)\,, \quad L_2(p) = \frac{1}{6}\,(p+1)\,p(p-1)\,.$$

Tables of $L_i(p)$ are available, e.g. to $10\,D$ at an interval of 0.0001 in p in NATIONAL BUREAU OF STANDARDS (1948).

It can be shown that such tables are unnecessary and that $n+1$-point interpolation can be arranged as a succession of linear interpolations. This scheme is due to A. C. AITKEN, and is outlined in **Problems 6.4 to 6.8.**

The practice of interpolation is discussed in many books, e.g. NAUTICAL ALMANAC OFFICE (1956), NATIONAL PHYSICAL LABORATORY (1961), FOX (1956), and we shall confine our attention mainly to some rather theoretical questions.

A generalization of the error estimate (6.1) can be obtained for an n-point Lagrangian interpolation:

$$f(x) - L_n(f,\, x) = \frac{f^{(n)}(\zeta)}{n!}\,(x-x_1)\,(x-x_2)\cdots(x-x_n) \tag{6.2}$$

assuming the existence of $f^{(n)}(x)$ in an interval including the distinct nodes $x_1, x_2, \ldots, x_n$, and the current point x; ζ is a point in this interval, whose position depends on x.

The derivation of the expression for the interpolant $L_n(f,\, x)$ and the remainder depend essentially on the fact that the nodes are distinct. It is interesting to consider what happens when we permit multiple nodes, and consider *osculatory* interpolation when not only the interpolant but also some of its derivatives coincide with the object function and its corresponding derivatives. We discuss the Hermitian case only. (For the extreme case of confluence see **Problem 6.3.**)

A simple counting argument shows that one might expect to find a unique polynomial $H = H_{2n+1}(f, x)$ of degree $2n + 1$ which satisfies

$$H(x_i) = f(x_i), \quad H'(x_i) = f'(x_i)$$

for $n + 1$ distinct values $x_0, x_1, \ldots, x_n$. This can indeed be established along the lines used in the two proofs of (1.3). If

$$l_i(x) = \prod [(x - x_j)/(x_i - x_j)]$$

where the product is over all $j \neq i$, $j = 0, 1, 2, \ldots, n$, then

$$H(x) = \sum \{l_i(x)\}^2 \{1 - 2 l_i'(x_i) (x - x_i)\} a_i + \sum \{l_i(x)\}^2 (x - x_i) b_i$$

where the sums are for $i = 0, 1, 2, \ldots, n$, is a polynomial $H(x)$ of degree $2n + 1$, such that

$$H(x_i) = a_i, \quad H'(x_i) = b_i, \quad i = 0, 1, \ldots, n.$$

Similar arguments to those used in establishing (6.2) lead to the following error estimate:

$$f(x) - H(f, x) = \frac{f^{(2n+2)}(\zeta)}{(2n+2)!} (x - x_0)^2 (x - x_1)^2 \cdots (x - x_n)^2 \quad (6.3)$$

when $f^{(2n+2)}(x)$ exists in an interval including $x_0, x_1, \ldots, x_n$ and the current-point x and where $\zeta = \zeta(x)$ lies in this interval.

We outline the proof. We may assume x different from all the x_i, for otherwise (6.3) is trivial. Consider

$$F(z) = f(z) - H(f, z) - [f(x) - H(f, x)] \prod [(z - x_i)^2/(x - x_i)^2]$$

where the product is over $i = 0, 1, 2, \ldots, n$. It is clear that $F(x) = 0$ and $F(x_i) = 0$, $i = 0, 1, 2, \ldots, n$. It follows from ROLLE's Theorem that $F'(z)$ vanishes for $(n + 1)$ distinct values of z, none of which coincide with any x_i. It is obvious that $F'(x_i) = 0$, $i = 0, 1, 2, \ldots, n$. Hence $F'(z)$ vanishes for $(2n + 2)$ distinct values of z, in the interval containing x and the x_i, $i = 0, 1, 2, \ldots, n$. Repeated application of ROLLE's Theorem shows that $F^{(2n+2)}(z)$ must vanish at some point ζ in this interval. We note that $H(f, z)$ is a polynomial of degree $(2n + 1)$ at most and so $H^{(2n+2)} = 0$. Since $\prod (z - x_i)^2$ is a polynomial of degree $(2n + 2)$ with leading coefficient unity, it follows that its $(2n + 2)$th derivative is $(2n + 2)!$ Hence

$$0 = F^{(2n+2)}(\zeta) = f^{(2n+2)}(\zeta) - (2n + 2)! [f(x) - H(f, x)] \prod (x - x_i)^{-2}$$

which gives (6.3).

With the estimates (6.2) and (6.3) available we can discuss some problems about the optimal choice of the nodes.

(6.1) Suppose we are going to interpolate in $[-1, 1]$, using an n-point Lagrangian formula, for a function $f(x)$, whose n-th derivative is bounded in $[-1, 1]$. What is the 'best' choice of $x_1, x_2, \ldots, x_n$?

From (6.2) it follows that this choice is that which minimizes the maximum of

$$\left| (x - x_1) (x - x_2) \cdots (x - x_n) \right|, \quad -1 \leq x \leq 1 .$$

This means [cf. **(3.1)**] that the x_i should be taken as the zeros of $T_n(x)$, i.e.,

$$x_i = \cos\{(2 i - 1) \pi/2 n\}, \quad i = 1, 2, \ldots, n .$$

(6.2) Suppose that we are going to interpolate in $[-1, 1]$, using an n-point Hermite formula, for a function $f(x)$, whose $2 n$-th derivative is bounded in $[-1, 1]$. What is the best choice of $x_1, x_2, \ldots, x_n$ if we measure the error as the integral over x? That is, we want to minimize

$$\left\{ \max_{-1 \leq x \leq 1} \left| f^{(2 n)}(x) \right| / (2 n) ! \right\} \times \int_{-1}^{+1} (x - x_1)^2 \cdots (x - x_n)^2 \, dx .$$

It follows from **(5.7)** that the x_i should be taken as the zeros of the Legendre polynomial $P_n(x)$.

(6.3) Finally, let us discuss the effect of errors in the values at the nodes in the Lagrangian case. We have

$$\delta f(x) = \sum l_i(x) \, \delta f_i$$

and so, if ε is a bound for the errors in the f_i we have

$$\left| \delta f(x) \right| \leq \varepsilon \sum \left| l_i(x) \right| .$$

It is possible to discuss

$$\max_x \sum \left| l_i(x) \right|$$

in any particular case. For instance, with $n = 11$, and equally spaced nodes, we have $\max \sum \left| l_i(x) \right| \doteq 25$. See NATIONAL BUREAU OF STANDARDS (1948).

We note, following FRÉCHET (1920), that the relative error under consideration even for a single non-zero δf_i, can be arbitrarily large, for n sufficiently large, in the equally spaced case, for points occupying about half of the interval. Note that this error depends only on the choice of the nodes, and appears for any function. The proof of this statement is elementary but complicated.

It is natural to ask how to choose the x_i so that this type of error is minimized in some sense. A complete solution to this question does not seem to be available, but it can be answered if we confine our attention to the case of genuine *extrapolation*. See BERNSTEIN (1926).

The result which can be obtained is that the nodes in the minimizing case are the zeros of

$$w(x) = (x^2 - 1)\, U_{n-1}(x) \ .$$

In this case it can be shown that outside $[-1, 1]$ we have

$$\sum | l_i(x) | \leq | T_n(x) | \ .$$

Interpolation processes. The way in which we try $(n+1)$-point interpolation if n-point is not satisfactory suggests a study of a sequence of (Lagrangian) interpolation processes defined by a sequence of nodes:

$$x_1^{(1)} \,;\ x_1^{(2)},\, x_2^{(2)} \,;\ x_1^{(3)},\, x_2^{(3)},\, x_3^{(3)} \,;\ \ldots,$$

all in a fixed interval $[a, b]$. Suppose we pick on a special function $f(x)$, defined in $[a, b]$ and we consider for $n = 1, 2, \ldots$ the Lagrangian interpolant of degree $n-1$, $L_n(f, x)$, with nodes $x_1^{(n)}, x_2^{(n)}, \ldots, x_n^{(n)}$. We can ask whether

(6.4) $$L_n(f, x) \to f(x) \quad \text{as} \quad n \to \infty$$

for any or all of the points $x \in [a, b]$. There are many questions and some solutions to problems of this kind. We prove two positive results.

(6.5)   *If $f(x)$ is a polynomial (6.4) is true for all x.*

Proof. For if $f(x)$ has degree N then for $n \geq N$, $L_n(f, x) \equiv f(x)$ and the sequence $\{L_n(f, x)\}$ is stationary and therefore convergent.

(6.6)   *If $f(x)$ is any continuous function, we can choose the $x_m^{(n)}$ so that (6.4) will be true uniformly in $[a, b]$.*

Proof. By the fundamental Chebyshev theorem, for each n, there is a polynomial $\pi_n(x)$ of best approximation to $f(x)$. We know that the difference $\pi_n(x) - f(x)$ vanishes $n+1$ times in $[a, b]$: these zeros we take to be the $x_m^{(n+1)}$. This means that the corresponding $L_{n+1}(f, x)$ is forced to be $\pi_n(x)$. But we know that $\{\pi_n(x)\}$ converges uniformly to $f(x)$.

We list without proof some negative results.

(6.7)   *No matter what the $x_m^{(n)}$ are, there are continuous functions $f(x)$ for which (6.4) is not true uniformly in $[a, b]$.*

(6.8)   *If $f(x) = | x |$ and the $x_m^{(n)}$ are equally spaced in $[-1, 1]$ there is convergence only at $0, \pm 1$.*

(6.9)   *If $f(x) = (1 + x^2)^{-1}$ and the $x_m^{(n)}$ are equally spaced in $[-5, 5]$ then the sequence $\{L_n(f, x)\}$ is divergent if $| x | > 3.6334 \ldots$*

(6.10)   *If the $x_m^{(n)}$ are the Chebyshev abscissae, there are continuous functions for which (6.4) is always false.*

To conclude this chapter on a more cheerful note we show that if we confine our attention to an interpolation scheme based on the zeros of the polynomials $\pi_1(x)$, $\pi_2(x)$, ... orthogonal with respect to $w(x)$ on $[a, b]$, then (6.4) is true in a certain sense for every continuous function $f(x)$.

(6.11)   (ERDÖS-TURÁN, 1937). *For every continuous $f(x)$ we have*

$$\lim_{n \to \infty} \int_a^b w(x) \{L_{\pi_n}(f, x) - f(x)\}^2 \, dx = 0$$

where $L_{\pi_n}(f, x)$ denotes the Lagrangian polynomial coinciding with f at the zeros of $\pi_n(x)$.

Proof. We denote by $p_n(x)$ the polynomial of best approximation (of degree $\leq n$) to $f(x)$ in $[a, b]$ and write

$$E_n = \max_{a \leq x \leq b} |f(x) - p_n(x)|.$$

We have

$$|p_{n-1}(x) - f(x)| \leq E_{n-1},$$

$$\int_a^b w(x) [p_{n-1}(x) - f(x)]^2 \, dx \leq E_{n-1}^2 \int_a^b w(x) \, dx.$$

Now $p_{n-1}(x) \equiv L_{\pi_n}(p_{n-1}, x)$ and so:

$$L_{\pi_n}(f, x) - p_{n-1}(x) = \sum_{k=1}^{n} [f(x_k) - p_{n-1}(x_k)] l_k(x)$$

where $l_k(x) = \pi_n(x)/\pi_n'(x_k) (x - x_k)$. From **Problem 5.12** (i) we have

$$\int_a^b [L_{\pi_n}(f, x) - p_{n-1}(x)]^2 w(x) \, dx$$

$$= \sum_{k=1}^{n} \left\{ [f(x_k) - p_{n-1}(x_k)]^2 \int_a^b w(x) [l_k(x)]^2 \, dx \right\}.$$

By **Problem 5.12** (ii) and our choice of p_{n-1}, we see that

$$\int_a^b w(x) \{L_{\pi_n}(f, x) - p_{n-1}(x)\}^2 \, dx \leq E_{n-1}^2 \int_a^b w(x) \, dx.$$

Using the fact that $(A + B)^2 \leq 2 (A^2 + B^2)$ we obtain

$$\int_a^b w(x) \{L_{\pi_n}(f, x) - f(x)\}^2 \, dx \leq 4 E_{n-1}^2 \int_a^b w(x) \, dx,$$

from which our theorem follows.

Chapter 6. Problems

6.1 Evaluate the first 5 Lagrange interpolation polynomials for the function $|x|$, in the interval $[-1, 1]$, where the nodes are equally spaced, i.e.,

$$0; \quad -1, 1; \quad -1, 0, 1; \quad 1 - \frac{1}{3}, +\frac{1}{3}, 1; \quad 1, -\frac{1}{2}, 0, \frac{1}{2}, 1 .$$

6.2 The same as **Problem 6.1**, for $(1 + x^2)^{-1}$.

6.3 Formulate, and establish a result suggested by letting *all* the nodes $x_0, x_1, \ldots, x_n$ coincide in the Lagrange interpolation problem.

6.4 Establish AITKEN's algorithm for Lagrangian interpolation in the following manner (FELLER). We have to evaluate $f(X)$, where f is a polynomial of degree n determined by its values at the distinct points $x_0, x_1, \ldots, x_n$, and X is a point different from these. Show that

$$f^{(1)}(x) = \frac{\begin{vmatrix} f(x_0) & x_0 - X \\ f(x) & x - X \end{vmatrix}}{(x - x_0)}$$

is (1) a polynomial of degree $n - 1$ (and therefore determined by its values at $x_1, x_2, \ldots, x_n$); (2) $f^{(1)}(X) = f(X)$.

Repetition of this process reduces the general interpolation process to linear interpolation.

6.5 Interpret AITKEN's process geometrically.

6.6 Use AITKEN's process to find $f(2.5)$ given that f is a cubic and $f(1) = 1$, $f(2) = 125$, $f(3) = 729$, $f(4) = 2197$. Complete the table:

$$1 = x_0 \qquad 1 = f(x_0)$$

$$2 = x_1 \qquad 125 = f(x_1) \qquad 187 = f^{(1)}(x_1)$$

$$3 = x_2 \qquad 729 = f(x_2) \qquad 547 = f^{(1)}(x_2) \qquad 367 = f^{(2)}(x_2)$$

$$4 = x_4 \qquad 2197 = f(x_3) \qquad\qquad ? \qquad\qquad\qquad ? \qquad\qquad\qquad ?$$

6.7 Use AITKEN's process to find $f(2.5)$ given:

$$f(1) = -1491, \quad f(2) = -575, \quad f(3) = 661, \quad f(4) = 2265 .$$

6.8 Use AITKEN's process for *inverse* interpolation to find the zero of $f(x)$ where

$$f(0) = -342, \quad f(1) = -218, \quad f(2) = 386, \quad f(3) = 1854 .$$

Show that the values of $f(x)$ given are those of a cubic and hence find the zero directly. Explain any discrepancy between this result and that obtained by AITKEN's Method.

6.9   Write down an expression for the error $f(x) - L_n(f,x)$ in the Lagrangian interpolation for a function $f(x)$, for which $f^{(11)}(x)$ exists, at the points which are the zeros of $T_{10}(x)$. Assuming that $|f^{(11)}(x)| \leq 1$ find an estimate for the numerical value of this error at a point x_1, $-1 \leq x_1 \leq 1$. What are the corresponding numerical values when the nodes are (i) the zeros of $U_{10}(x)$, (ii) the zeros of $P_{10}(x)$ and (iii) the points ± 1, $\pm 7/9$, $\pm 5/9$, $\pm 3/9$, $\pm 1/9$?

6.10   The following is a portion of table of a function $(J_0(x))$ and its derivative:

x	$J_0(x)$	$J_0'(x)$
1.4	0.56685 51204	-0.54194 77139
1.5	0.51182 76717	-0.55793 65079 .

Evaluate $J_0(1.45)$ by linear interpolation and by two-point Hermite interpolation.

CHAPTER 7

The Bernoulli Polynomials

The Bernoulli Numbers and Polynomials will be introduced formally. The following results are familiar

$$1 + 2 + \cdots + n = \frac{1}{2} n(n + 1), \quad 1^2 + 2^2 + \cdots + n^2 = \frac{1}{6} n(n + 1)(2n + 1),$$

$$1^3 + 2^3 + \cdots + n^3 = \left[\frac{n(n + 1)}{2}\right]^2.$$

It is natural to seek expressions for

$$1^r + 2^r + \cdots + n^r, \tag{7.0}$$

or, more generally,

$$f(1) + f(2) + \cdots + f(x).$$

Suppose the latter sum is $F(x)$. Then

$$\Delta F(x) = F(x + 1) - F(x) = f(x + 1).$$

Using the operator $D = (d/dx)$ a symbolic form of Taylor's Series is:

$$F(x + 1) = F(x) + D F(x) + \frac{1}{2!} D^2 F(x) + \cdots$$

$$= e^D F(x).$$

Similarly $f(x + 1) = e^D f(x)$. Hence we have $(e^D - 1) F(x) = e^D f(x)$, i.e.

$$F(x) = \left(\frac{e^D}{e^D - 1}\right) f(x) = \left(1 + \frac{1}{e^D - 1}\right) f(x).$$

We could define the *Bernoulli Numbers* to be the coefficients in the expansion of $1 + (e^D - 1)^{-1}$, in powers of D. It is, however, more convenient to use the following definition:

$$D(e^D - 1)^{-1} = \sum_{n=0}^{\infty} B_n D^n/n!,$$

so that

$$B_0 = 1, \quad B_1 = -\frac{1}{2}, \quad B_2 = \frac{1}{6}, \quad B_3 = B_5 = \cdots = 0,$$

$$B_4 = -\frac{1}{30}, \quad B_6 = \frac{1}{42}, \quad B_8 = -\frac{1}{30}, \quad B_{10} = \frac{5}{66}, \ldots.$$

Todd 5

It is important to bear in mind that many different normalizations are in common use, and to take corresponding care in the use of formulae.

We follow the notation of ERDÉLYI (1953).

It is natural to introduce the *Bernoulli Polynomials* by a similar generating function:

$$\frac{t\, e^{xt}}{e^t - 1} = \sum_{n=0}^{\infty} B_n(x)\, \frac{t^n}{n!}\, , \quad |t| < 2\,\pi\, . \tag{7.1}$$

It is clear that we have

$$B_n = B_n(0)$$

and the initial polynomials are

$$B_0(x) = 1\, , \quad B_1(x) = x - \frac{1}{2}\, , \quad B_2(x) = x^2 - x + \frac{1}{6}\, ,$$

$$B_3(x) = x^3 - \frac{3}{2}\, x^2 + \frac{1}{2}\, x\, , \quad B_4(x) = x^4 - 2\, x^3 + x^2 - \frac{1}{30}\, .$$

With the present normalization the answer to our original problem is

$$\sum_{k=0}^{m} k^n = \frac{B_{n+1}(m+1) - B_{n+1}}{n+1}\, , \quad n = 1, 2, \ldots, \tag{7.2}$$

entirely analogous to

$$\int_{1}^{m} t^n\, dt = \frac{m^{n+1} - 1}{n+1}\, .$$

The result (7.2) can be obtained as follows. From (7.1), putting $x + 1$ for x we have

$$\frac{t\, e^{xt} \times e^t}{e^t - 1} = \sum_{n=0}^{\infty} B_n(x+1)\, t^n/n!$$

and so

$$\sum_{n=1}^{\infty} \frac{x^{n-1}\, t^n}{(n-1)!} = t\, e^{xt} = \frac{t\, e^{(x+1)t}}{e^t - 1} - \frac{t\, e^{xt}}{e^t - 1} = \sum_{n=0}^{\infty} [B_n(x+1) - B_n(x)]\, t^n/n!\, .$$

Comparing coefficients of $t, t^2, \ldots$ we find

$$B_n(x+1) - B_n(x) = n\, x^{n-1}, \quad n = 1, 2, \ldots\, . \tag{7.3}$$

If we put $x = 0$ in this relation we get

$$B_n(1) = B_n\, , \quad n = 0, 1, 2, \ldots\, . \tag{7.3}_0$$

If we differentiate (7.1) with respect to x we get

$$\frac{t^2\, e^{xt}}{e^t - 1} = \sum_{n=0}^{\infty} B_n'(x)\, \frac{t^n}{n!}\, , \quad \text{i.e.,} \quad t \sum_{n=0}^{\infty} B_n(x)\, \frac{t^n}{n!} = \sum_{n=0}^{\infty} B_n'(x)\, \frac{t^n}{n!}$$

and, comparing coefficients,

$$B_n'(x) = n \, B_{n-1}(x) \, , \quad n = 1, 2, \ldots \, . \tag{7.4}$$

Integrating (7.4) between x, $x+1$ we get

$$B_n(x+1) - B_n(x) = n \int_x^{x+1} B_{n-1}(t) \, dt$$

which, combined with (7.3), gives

$$\int_x^{x+1} B_r(t) \, dt = x^r \, . \tag{7.5}$$

If we sum (7.5) for $x = 1, 2, \ldots, n$, we get

$$\int_1^{n+1} B_r(t) \, dt = 1^r + 2^r + \cdots + n^r$$

and using $(7.3)_0$, (7.4) we obtain (7.2) as required.

We note here that an entirely similar theory of *Euler Numbers* E_n and *Euler Polynomials* $E_n(x)$ can be constructed if, instead of beginning with (7.0), we considered

$$1^r - 2^r + 3^r - \cdots + (-1)^{n-1} n^r \, . \tag{7.0'}$$

The generating function corresponding to (7.1) is

$$\frac{2 \, e^{xt}}{e^t + 1} = \sum_{n=0}^{\infty} E_n(x) \, \frac{t^n}{n!} \, , \quad |t| < \pi \, , \tag{7.1'}$$

and the following results can be obtained:

$$\sum_{k=1}^{r} (-1)^{r-k} k^n = \frac{E_n \, (r+1) + (-1)^{n+r-1} E_n(0)}{2} \, , \quad r, n = 1, 2, \ldots, \tag{7.2'}$$

$$E_n(x+1) + E_n(x) = 2 \, x^n \, , \tag{7.3'}$$

$$E_n'(x) = n \, E_{n-1}(x) \, . \tag{7.4'}$$

We define the Euler numbers E_n by $E_n = 2^n \, E_n(1/2)$ and find

$$E_0 = 1 \, , \quad E_2 = -1 \, , \quad E_4 = 5 \, , \quad E_6 = -61 \, ,$$
$$E_8 = 1385 \, , \ldots, \quad E_{2n+1} = 0 \, , \quad n = 0, 1, 2, \ldots \, .$$

Fourier Series. A change of scale in **Problem 5.1** gives

$$B_1(x) = x - \frac{1}{2} = -\sum_{r=1}^{\infty} \frac{\sin 2\pi r x}{r \pi} \, , \quad 0 < x < 1 \, . \tag{7.6}$$

(Note that although the evaluation of the *F.C.* is trivial, the proof of convergence of the *F.S.* is not, and, even more difficult is the actual summation of the series, i.e. to prove it converges to the 'correct' sum.)

If we calculate the *F.C.* of $B_2(x)$ we find that

$$B_2(x) = x^2 - x + \frac{1}{6} = 4 \sum_{r=1}^{\infty} \frac{\cos 2 \pi r x}{(2 \pi r)^2} \, . \qquad (7.7)$$

(Convergence, and convergence to the 'correct' sum is much easier to prove in this case.) If we calculate the *F.C.* of $B_3(x)$ we find that

$$B_3(x) = x^3 - \frac{3}{2} x^2 + \frac{1}{2} x = 12 \sum_{r=1}^{\infty} \frac{\sin 2 \pi r x}{(2 \pi r)^3} \, . \qquad (7.8)$$

Results corresponding to (7.7) and (7.8) are available for general even and odd order Bernoulli polynomials: for $0 < x < 1$ we have

$$B_{2n}(x) = 2(-1)^{n+1} (2 n)! \sum_{r=1}^{\infty} (2 \pi r)^{-2n} \cos 2 \pi r x \, , \qquad (7.9)$$

$$B_{2n+1}(x) = 2(-1)^{n+1} (2 n + 1)! \sum_{r=1}^{\infty} (2 \pi r)^{-2n-1} \sin 2 \pi r x \, . \qquad (7.10)$$

If we put $x = 0$ in (7.9) and (7.10) we obtain, for $n = 1, 2, \ldots$,

$$B_{2n} = 2(-1)^{n+1} (2 n)! \sum_{r=1}^{\infty} (2 \pi r)^{-2n} \quad \text{or} \quad \sum_{r=1}^{\infty} r^{-2n} = (-1)^{n+1} \frac{(2 \pi)^{2n} B_{2n}}{2 (2 n)!}, \qquad (7.11)$$

$$B_{2n+1} = 0 \, . \qquad (7.12)$$

It is clear from (7.9) and (7.10) that we have

$$B_n(1 - x) = (-1)^n B_n(x) \, . \qquad (7.13)$$

Some other properties of the $B_n(x)$ are obtained by considering the equation

$$\sum_{n=0}^{\infty} B_n(x + 1) \frac{t^n}{n!} = \frac{t e^{xt} e^t}{e^t - 1} = e^t \frac{t e^{xt}}{e^t - 1} = \sum_{n=0}^{\infty} B_n(x) \frac{t^n}{n!} \sum_{m=0}^{\infty} \frac{t^m}{m!} \, .$$

If we multiply the two power series on the right by CAUCHY's Method (collecting terms on the diagonals SW—NE) we find, for $n = 2, 3, \ldots$,

$$B_n(x + 1) = \sum_{r=0}^{n} \binom{n}{r} B_r(x) \qquad (7.14)$$

or

$$\sum_{r=0}^{n-1} \binom{n}{r} B_r(x) = n \, x^{n-1} \, . \qquad (7.15)$$

We can specialize these to get a recurrence relation for the Bernoulli numbers:

$$\sum_{r=0}^{n-1} \binom{n}{r} B_r = 0 , \quad n \geq 2 . \tag{7.16}$$

We conclude this chapter with two accounts of the Euler-Maclaurin Sum Formula—one formal and one rigorous—and as an application of it we shall obtain STIRLING's Formula.

At the beginning of this chapter we noted the relations

$$F(1) = e^D F(0) , \quad \text{i. e.,} \quad f(0) = F(1) - F(0) = (e^D - 1) F(0) ,$$

and

$$\Delta F(0) = F(1) - F(0) = f(0) .$$

These suggest that

$$\Delta = e^D - 1$$

and we have

$$F = \Delta^{-1} f = (e^D - 1)^{-1} f = D^{-1} [1 + D/2! + D^2/3! + \cdots]^{-1} f$$

$$= \left[D^{-1} - \frac{1}{2} + D/12 - D^3/720 + \cdots \right] f$$

$$= \int f(x) \, dx - \frac{1}{2} f + f'/12 - f'''/720 + \cdots .$$

Hence, subtracting,

$$f(0) + f(1) + \cdots + f(n-1) = \int_0^n f(x) \, dx - \frac{1}{2} f(n) + \frac{1}{2} f(0)$$

$$+ \frac{1}{12} [f'(n) - f'(0)]$$

$$- \frac{1}{720} [f'''(n) - f'''(0)]$$

$$+ \cdots ,$$

which is the formula required.

We shall now give a rigorous derivation of the sum formula. We follow KNOPP (1928). Suppose $f'(x)$ is continuous on $[0, n]$. Then

$$\int_{r-1}^r f'(t) \, dt = f(r) - f(r-1) , \quad r = 1, 2, \ldots, n .$$

If we multiply this across by r and then sum we get

$$\sum_{r=1}^n \int_{r-1}^r r f'(t) \, dt = \sum_{r=1}^n r(f(r) - f(r-1))$$

$$= - (f(0) + f(1) + \cdots + f(n)) + (n+1) f(n) .$$

We may write $r = [t] + 1$ in the integrals so that

$$f(0) + f(1) + \cdots + f(n) = (n + 1) f(n) - \int_0^n ([t] + 1) f'(t) \, dt \qquad (7.17)$$

where [ ] means 'integral part of'. Now

$$\int_0^n t f'(t) \, dt = n f(n) - \int_0^n f(t) \, dt . \qquad (7.18)$$

Hence, substituting from (7.18) in (7.17) we get

$$f(0) + f(1) + \cdots + f(n)$$

$$= \int_0^n f(t) \, dt + \frac{1}{2} (f(0) + f(n)) + \int_0^n \left(t - [t] - \frac{1}{2} \right) f'(t) \, dt . \qquad (7.19)$$

It is clear that $t - [t] - 1/2$ has period unity and for $0 < t < 1$ we have

$$t - [t] - \frac{1}{2} = t - \frac{1}{2} = B_1(t) .$$

For the rest of this chapter we shall denote by $\bar{B}_n(t)$ the function which coincides with $B_n(t)$ in $[0, 1)$ and has period 1, i.e., the *F.S.* given by (7.9) and (7.10). We can rewrite (7.19) as

$$f(0) + f(1) + \cdots + f(n) = \int_0^n f(t) \, dt + \frac{1}{2} (f(0) + f(n)) + \int_0^n \bar{B}_1(t) f'(t) \, dt . \quad (7.19')$$

The next stage in our development is to assume that $f'''(x)$ is continuous. We take the last term on the right in (7.19′) and integrate by parts; this has to be done with some care.

It is clear, e.g., from (7.5), that

$$\int_0^1 B_n(t) \, dt = 0 .$$

It now follows that $\int_0^x \bar{B}_n(t) \, dt$ has period 1 and indeed that

$$\bar{B}_n(x) = \int_0^x n \, \bar{B}_{n-1}(t) \, dt .$$

We have, therefore,

$$\int_0^n \bar{B}_1(t)\, f'(t)\, dt = \left[\frac{\bar{B}_2(t)}{2}\, f'(t) \right]_0^n - \int_0^n \frac{\bar{B}_2(t)}{2}\, f''(t)\, dt$$

$$= \frac{B_2}{2}\, [f'(n) - f'(0)] - \int_0^n \frac{\bar{B}_2(t)}{2}\, f''(t)\, dt$$

$$= \frac{1}{12}\, [f'(n) - f'(0)] - \left[\frac{\bar{B}_3(t)}{6}\, f''(t) \right]_0^n + \int_0^n \frac{\bar{B}_3(t)}{6}\, f'''(t)\, dt$$

$$= \frac{1}{12}\, [f'(n) - f'(0)] + \int_0^n \bar{B}_3(t)\, f'''(t)\, dt/6 .$$

It is clear that we can continue in this manner and we obtain

$$f(0) + f(1) + \cdots + f(n)$$

$$= \int_0^n f(t)\, dt + \frac{1}{2}\, (f(n) + f(0)) + \frac{B_2}{2!}\, (f'(n) - f'(0))$$

$$+ \frac{B_4}{4!}\, (f'''(n) - f'''(0)) + \cdots \tag{7.20}$$

$$+ \frac{B_{2k}}{(2k)!}\, (f^{(2k-1)}(n) - f^{(2k-1)}(0)) + R_k$$

where

$$(2k+1)!\, R_k = \int_0^n \bar{B}_{2k+1}(t)\, f^{(2k+1)}(t)\, dt . \tag{7.21}$$

This is the Euler-Maclaurin sum formula.

We shall now investigate the behaviour of the remainder R_k, in a special case which is often of interest:

$f(x)$ is to have a constant sign for $x > 0$ and $f^{(r)}(x)$ tends steadily to zero as $x \to \infty$, for $r = 0, 1, 2, \ldots$. (7.22)

We begin by showing that $B_n(x)$ has the following behavior in $[0, 1]$:

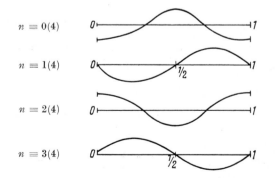

[The non-trivial zeros of the $B_n(x)$ have been studied by D. H. LEHMER, INKERI, LENSE and OSTROWSKI.] It is easy to verify directly the indicated behavior for $n = 2, 3, 4, 5$. The proof is by induction in steps of two. Assume that the behavior indicated has been established for $n \geq 2, n \leq 2m$. Then we consider B_{2m+1}. From the results (7.12), (7.13) we see that the zeros at $0, \frac{1}{2}, 1$ are located as desired. These are all the zeros in $[0, 1]$ for if there were (at least) one more, by symmetry, there would have to be two, and ROLLE'S Theorem [and the relation $B_n'(x) = n B_{n-1}(x)$] would show that there were at least four zeros of B_{2m}, which contradicts our induction assumption. It follows from the relations $B_n'(x) = n B_{n-1}(x)$ that $B_{2n+1}(x)$ for small x has the same sign as $B_{2n}(0) = B_{2n}$, i.e. $(-1)^{n+1}$. These remarks establish the results for $2m + 1$ from those for $2m$. We now show how to get from $2m + 1$ to $2m + 2$. Since $B_{2m+2}'(x) = (2m + 2) B_{2m+1}(x)$ and since $B_{2m+1}(x)$ has exactly one interior zero, B_{2m+2} can have exactly one interior extremum, actually at $x = 1/2$. Now since

$$\int_0^1 B_{2m+2}(t)\, dt = 0 \, ,$$

the integrand must change sign. Since $B_{2m+2}(0) = B_{2m+2}$ and has sign $(-1)^{m+2} = (-1)^m$ the sign of the extrema $B_{2m+2}(1/2)$ is opposite, i.e. $(-1)^{m+1}$. This establishes the step from $2m + 1$ to $2m + 2$ and completes the proof.

It is a consequence of our assumption (7.22) that the derivatives $f^{(r)}(x)$ must have constant sign. Indeed if $f > 0$, we have sign $f^{(r)}(x) = (-1)^r$ so that $f^{(2r)}(x) \to 0 +$ and $f^{(2r+1)}(x) \to 0 -$ as $x \to \infty$.

Consider in the light of these remarks, and our diagrams:

$$(2k + 1)!\, R_k = \int_0^n B_{2k+1}(t)\, f^{(2k+1)}(t)\, dt \, . \tag{7.23}$$

In any interval $[r - 1, r]$, $\bar{B}_{2k+1}(t)$ behaves like $B_{2k+1}(t)$ and is symmetrical about $t = 1/2$. Since $f^{(2k+1)}(t) \to 0 -$ it is clear that the contribution of each interval $[r - 1, r]$ to the integral in (7.23) has the same sign, in fact $(-1)^k$, and this therefore is the sign of R_k. It follows that

$$\left| R_k \right| < \left| R_k - R_{k+1} \right| \, .$$

If we write down (7.20) with k replaced by $k + 1$ and subtract this from (7.20) we get

$$R_k - R_{k+1} = \frac{B_{2k+2}}{(2k + 2)!}\, [f^{(2k+1)}(n) - f^{(2k+1)}(0)] \, .$$

This expression exceeds R_k in absolute value, but has the same sign. Hence, for some θ, $0 \leq \theta \leq 1$:

$$R_k = \theta\, [R_k - R_{k+1}] = \theta\, \frac{B_{2k+2}}{(2k + 2)!}\, [f^{(2k+1)}(n) - f^{(2k+1)}(0)] \, .$$

We shall now derive a simple version of STIRLING's Formula. Henceforth all logarithms are natural, i.e. to base e. Using (7.19') with $f(x) = \log(1 + x)$ and the fact

$$\frac{d}{dx}[(1 + x)\log(1 + x) - x] = \log(1 + x)$$

we obtain first

$$\log 1 + \cdots + \log n = \int_0^{n-1} \log(1 + x)\,dx + \frac{1}{2}(\log 1 + \log n) + \int_0^{n-1} \overline{B}_1(x)\,dx/(1 + x)$$

and then

$$\log n! = n\log n - n + 1 + \frac{1}{2}\log n + \int_1^n \overline{B}_1(x)\,dx/x.$$

Now the integral can be regarded as the sum of the first $2(n - 1)$ terms of an 'alternating series'. Hence the integral

$$\int_1^\infty \overline{B}_1(x)\,dx/x$$

exists and we have

$$\log n! - \left[\left(n + \frac{1}{2}\right)\log n - n + 1\right] = \int_1^\infty \overline{B}_1(x)\,dx/x - \varepsilon_n \qquad (7.24)$$

where

$$\varepsilon_n = \int_n^\infty \overline{B}_1(x)\,dx/x$$

and $\varepsilon_n \to 0$. The evaluation of

$$I = \int_1^\infty \overline{B}_1(x)\,dx/x$$

is rather tricky. We use WALLIS' Formula in the form

$$\frac{2^{4n} \times (n!)^4}{((2n)!)^2(2n + 1)} \to \frac{1}{2}\pi.$$

Taking logarithms and using (7.24) we find

$$4n\log 2 + 4\left(n + \frac{1}{2}\right)\log n - 4n + 4 + 4I - 4\varepsilon_n$$

$$- 2\left[\left(2n + \frac{1}{2}\right)\log 2n - 2n + 1 + I - \varepsilon_{2n}\right] - \log(2n + 1) \to \log\frac{1}{2}\pi.$$

Simplifying and noting that

$$\log(2n + 1) - \log 2 - \log n = \log\left(1 + \frac{1}{2n}\right) \to 0$$

we get

$$2I = -2 + \log 2\pi, \quad I = \log\sqrt{2\pi} - 1$$

and so

$$\log n! = \left(n + \frac{1}{2}\right)\log n - n + \log \sqrt{2\pi} - \int_n^\infty \bar{B}_1(x)\, dx/x \qquad (7.25)$$

which can be written as

$$n! \sim \left(\frac{n}{e}\right)^n \sqrt{2\pi n}, \qquad n \to \infty. \qquad (7.25')$$

We can estimate the error

$$J_n = \int_n^\infty \bar{B}_1(x)\, dx/x$$

in the following way. (Draw diagrams to clarify the argument.) We have

$$J_n = \sum_{r=n}^\infty (J_r - J_{r+1})$$

and

$$J_r - J_{r+1} = \int_r^{r+1} \bar{B}_1(x)\, dx/x = \left[\int_r^{r+1/2} + \int_{r+1/2}^{r+1}\right]\bar{B}_1(x)\, dx/x$$

$$= -\int_{1/2}^0 \frac{\bar{B}_1\left(r + \frac{1}{2} - y\right)}{r + \frac{1}{2} - y}\, dy + \int_0^{1/2} \frac{\bar{B}_1\left(r + \frac{1}{2} + z\right)}{r + \frac{1}{2} + z}\, dz$$

$$= \int_0^{1/2}\left\{\frac{B_1\left(\frac{1}{2} - y\right)}{r + \frac{1}{2} - y} + \frac{B_1\left(\frac{1}{2} + y\right)}{r + \frac{1}{2} + y}\right\} dy$$

$$= -\int_0^{1/2}\left\{\left(r + \frac{1}{2} - y\right)^{-1} - \left(r + \frac{1}{2} + y\right)^{-1}\right\} y\, dy$$

$$= -2\int_0^{1/2} y^2\left\{\left(r + \frac{1}{2}\right)^2 - y^2\right\}^{-1} dy.$$

Thus

$$-J_n = \sum_{r=n}^\infty \int_0^{1/2} \frac{2\, y^2\, dy}{\left(r + \frac{1}{2}\right)^2 - y^2} < \sum_{r=n}^\infty r^{-2}\int_0^{1/2} 2\, y^2\, dy = \sum_{r=n}^\infty r^{-2}/12.$$

Now since

$$\left(r - \frac{1}{2}\right)^{-1} - \left(r + \frac{1}{2}\right)^{-1} = \left(r^2 - \frac{1}{4}\right)^{-1} > r^{-2}$$

we have

$$0 < -J_n < \frac{1}{12}\sum_{r=n}^\infty\left\{\left(r - \frac{1}{2}\right)^{-1} - \left(r + \frac{1}{2}\right)^{-1}\right\} = \frac{1}{12}\left(n - \frac{1}{2}\right)^{-1}. \qquad (7.26)$$

Chapter 7. Problems

7.1 Express the coefficients in the expansions

$$\frac{1}{2} t \cot \frac{1}{2} t = 1 - \frac{1}{12} t^2 - \cdots ,$$

$$\tan \frac{1}{2} t = \frac{1}{2} t - \frac{1}{24} t^3 - \cdots$$

in terms of the B_n, and those in

$$\sec t = 1 + \frac{1}{2} t^2 + \cdots$$

in terms of the E_n.

7.2 Examine the realism of the estimates of the remainder in STIRLING's Formula given by (7.26) by evaluating this expression for $n = 10$, $n = 100$, $n = 1000$ and comparing the values given by the first three terms of (7.25) with those given in standard tables.

7.3 Evaluate

$$\sum_{n=1}^{\infty} n^{-2}$$

by writing it as

$$\sum_{n=1}^{\infty} n^{-2} = (1 + 2^{-2} + \cdots + 9^{-2}) + \sum_{n=0}^{\infty} (10 + n)^{-2}$$

and applying a limiting case of the Euler-Maclaurin formula to the infinite series on the right.

7.4 Establish WALLIS' Product:

$$\frac{\pi}{2} = \lim_{n \to \infty} \left\{ \frac{2 \times 2 \times 4 \times 4 \times 6 \times 6 \times 8 \times 8 \cdots (2\,n)\,(2\,n)}{1 \times 3 \times 3 \times 5 \times 5 \times 7 \times 7 \times 9 \cdots (2\,n - 1)\,(2\,n + 1)} \right\}$$

by observing that when $0 \le \theta \le \pi/2$, $0 \le \cos\theta \le 1$ so that $\cos^{2n}\theta \ge \cos^{2n+1}\theta \ge \cos^{2n+2}\theta$ which implies $I_{2n} \ge I_{2n+1} \ge I_{2n+2}$, where

$$I_n = \int_0^{\pi/2} \cos^n \theta \, d\theta .$$

[Hint: $n I_n = (n - 1) I_{n-2}$.]

7.5 A die is tossed 180 times. Find the probability that the upturned face is a six exactly thirty times.

$$\left[\text{Hint: Estimate } \binom{180}{30} \left(\frac{1}{6}\right)^{30} \left(\frac{5}{6}\right)^{150} \text{ by STIRLING's formula.} \right]$$

7.6 Use STIRLING's Formula to show that the Lagrange polynomials $L_n(x)$ for $|x|$, with equally spaced nodes, $-1 = x_0 < x_1 < \cdots < x_n = 1$, converge to $|x|$ at $x = 0$ as $n \to \infty$.

CHAPTER 8

Function Spaces

A basic concept in mathematics is that of a *class* X (of *elements* x). Initially, in the general theory of classes, we disregard the nature of the elements, and their order and are only concerned with the 'size' of the classes: this leads to the theory of *cardinal numbers*. If we impose an order structure on the class by means of a table (or function or relation):

	x_2
	$\vdots$
x_1	... x_1 precedes x_2

we are led to the theory of *ordinal numbers*.

The imposition of an algebraic structure on a class, e.g., by a single (addition) table

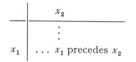

	x_2
	$\vdots$
x_1	... $x_1 + x_2$

leads to the idea of a *group*. If we impose in addition a multiplication table

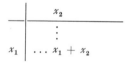

	x_2
	$\vdots$
x_1	... $x_1 \, x_2$

we are led to the ideas of *rings* and *fields*.

Note the importance of the axioms relating the two compositions.

Another development is the imposition of a geometrical or topological structure on classes. One way of doing this is by a distance function $\delta(x_1, x_2)$ which specifies the 'distance' between the two elements or 'points', x_1, x_2. A reasonable system of axioms is the following:

	x_2
	$\vdots$
x_1	... $\delta(x_1, x_2)$

Axioms: $\delta(x, y) = 0 \cdot \equiv \cdot x = y$

$\delta(x, y) = \delta(y, x) \geq 0$

$\delta(x, z) \leq \delta(x, y) + \delta(y, z)$

By means of this we can say directly when one element (point) of our class
—now a *metric space*—is near to another. This can be done less directly by
specifying the *closure* $\bar{A}$ of each sub-class $A \subset X$:

set	closure
ϕ	ϕ
$\vdots$	$\vdots$
A	$\bar{A}$
$\vdots$	$\vdots$
X	X

In terms of these concepts we can introduce the idea of limit, $\lim x_n$, and
convergence, $x_n \to \zeta$, in the *topological space* defined by the above table.

An abstract *linear vector space* is determined by a class X, and a coefficient
field F, together with two tables: one for vector addition and the other for
scalar multiplication

	β
	$\vdots$
α	$\ldots \alpha + \beta$

	a
	$\vdots$
α	$\ldots a\,\alpha$

with axioms for each, and for combined operations. The theory of finite
dimensional linear vector spaces is studied in detail in introductory courses
in linear algebra. If, in addition, we have a third operation: inner product

	β
	$\vdots$
α	$\ldots (\alpha, \beta)$

we are led to the study of what is essentially ordinary *euclidean geometry*
(of n dimensions).

By means of an inner product we can define a *norm* for each element
$\| x \| = (x, x)^{1/2}$. This norm could be introduced directly by a table

element	norm
0	0
$\vdots$	$\vdots$
x	$\| x \|$

Axioms:
$$\| x \| = 0 \cdot \equiv \cdot x = 0$$
$$\| a\,x \| = | a |\, \| x \|$$
$$\| x + y \| \leq \| x \| + \| y \| .$$

In terms of a norm we can introduce a distance function,

$$\delta(\alpha, \beta) = \| \alpha - \beta \| = (\alpha - \beta, \alpha - \beta)^{1/2} ,$$

which makes our space into a metric space in the sense specified above.

Much of the introductory material about linear vector spaces is independent of the idea of dimension and it is quite appropriate to consider *spaces of functions* which are usually not of finite dimension. We summarize the axioms for a linear vector space:

$$\alpha + \beta = \beta + \alpha \,,\, (\alpha + \beta) + \gamma = \alpha + (\beta + \gamma)\,,\, \alpha + 0 = \alpha,\, \alpha + (-\alpha) = 0$$

(vectors form an abelian group under addition);

$$(a_1 a_2) \times \alpha = a_1 \times (a_2 \times \alpha),\, 1 \times \alpha = \alpha\,;$$

$$a(\alpha + \beta) = a\alpha + a\beta\,,\, (a + b)\alpha = a\alpha + b\alpha \quad \text{(distributivity)}.$$

Examples

(1) All real functions of a real variable.
(2) All real functions continuous on a fixed interval $[a, b]$. This can be normed by putting $\|f\| = \max |f(x)|$.
(3) All polynomials defined on $[a, b]$.

It is clear that the space of all polynomials defined on $[a, b]$ does not have a finite basis. This is essentially the fundamental theorem of algebra. It is also clear from the Weierstrass approximation theorem that the set of all polynomials is *dense* in the set of all continuous functions (on a finite interval). By saying that a set A is dense in a metric space M we mean that given any $\varepsilon > 0$ and any $m \in M$ we can find an $a \in A$ such that

$$\delta(a, m) < \varepsilon\,.$$

(Compare the rational numbers on the line.)

(4) All real functions with period 2π.
(5) All real functions which have a continuous k-th derivative on $[a, b]$.
(6) c: The space of sequences $x = (x_1, x_2, \ldots)$ for which $\lim x_n$ exists. This is normed by setting $\|x\| = \max |x_i|$.
(7) l^2: The space of real sequences $x = (x_1, x_2, \ldots)$ for which $\sum x_i^2$ is convergent.
This is normed by setting

$$\|x\| = \sqrt{\sum x_i^2}\,.$$

This is an example of a Hilbert space. In virtue of the Schwarz inequality

$$\sum x_i^2 \sum y_i^2 \geq \left(\sum x_i y_i\right)^2$$

we can define an inner product

$$(x, y) = \sum x_i y_i$$

and verify that it satisfies the required postulates.

The following general problem of approximation has a meaning in a real normed linear vector space X. *Given an $f \in X$ and a set of linearly independent* *elements $b_1, b_2, \ldots, b_n$, all in X, find the linear combination $\sum \lambda_i b_i$ which is the best approximation (in the sense of the given norm) to f. That is, find:*

$$\min \left\| f - \sum \lambda_i b_i \right\|.$$

We shall show that this problem always has a solution. This includes as a special case the Chebyshev problem of Chapter 3 where $X = C$, the set of functions $f(x)$, continuous on $[a, b]$ with

$$\| f(x) \| = \max_{a \le x \le b} | f(x) |,$$

and where $b_i = x^{i-1}$. It is not possible to show that the solution to the general problem is unique. However we can establish uniqueness if we insist on our space being *strongly normed*, i.e., if

$$\| x + y \| = \| x \| + \| y \|, \quad x \ne 0, y \ne 0$$

only if $y = \alpha x$ $(\alpha \ge 0)$. Observe that this result does not give us uniqueness in the Chebyshev case for C is not strongly normed: indeed if $f(x_0) = \max | f(x) |$ *and* $g(x_0) = \max | g(x) |$ then $\| f + g \| = \| f \| + \| g \|$ and we can certainly choose $f \ne \alpha g$.

To establish the existence of a best approximation we first prove

(8.1) $\phi(\lambda_1, \ldots, \lambda_n) = \left\| f - \sum \lambda_i b_i \right\|$ *is a continuous function of its arguments.*

Proof. $\left| \phi(\Lambda) - \phi(\lambda) \right| = \left| \left\| f - \sum \Lambda_i b_i \right\| - \left\| f - \sum \lambda_i b_i \right\| \right|$

$$\le \left\| \sum (\Lambda_i - \lambda_i) b_i \right\|$$

$$\le \sum |\Lambda_i - \lambda_i| \| b_i \|$$

$$\le \max_{1 \le i \le n} |\Lambda_i - \lambda_i| \sum \| b_i \|.$$

The b_i's are fixed and so therefore is $\sum \| b_i \|$. Hence ϕ is continuous and, in particular,

$$\Psi(\lambda) = \left\| \sum \lambda_i b_i \right\|$$

is a continuous function of λ.

The *shell*

$$\lambda_1^2 + \lambda_2^2 + \cdots + \lambda_n^2 = 1$$

is a bounded closed set in ordinary n-dimensional space and on it the continuous function Ψ must assume its minimum, μ. Since $\Psi \ge 0$, $\mu \ge 0$. Since the b_i are linearly independent $\mu \ne 0$. Hence $\mu > 0$. It follows, by the homogeneity of the norm, that

$$\left\| \sum \lambda_i b_i \right\| \ge \mu \sqrt{\lambda_1^2 + \lambda_2^2 + \cdots + \lambda_n^2}. \tag{8.1}$$

Let ϱ be the lower bound of $\phi(\lambda)$. Then $\varrho \geq 0$ and we have to show that this bound is attained i.e. that there is a λ^* such that $\phi(\lambda^*) = \varrho$. We shall show that $\phi(\lambda)$ *is large* [specifically $\phi(\lambda) \geq \varrho + 1$] *when λ is large* [specifically, when $\sqrt{\sum \lambda_i^2} > R = (\varrho + 1 + \|f\|)/\mu$]. Hence the lower bound of $\phi(\lambda)$, for all λ, is the same as the lower bound when λ is restricted by $\sqrt{\sum \lambda_i^2} \leq R$ and we are now concerned with the lower bound of a continuous function on a *ball* (solid sphere). Since the ball is closed and bounded the lower bound is attained and the existence of λ^* is established.

To establish the statement in italics we observe that when λ is restricted to $\sqrt{\sum \lambda_i^2} \geq R$ we have, by (**8.1**),

$$\phi(\lambda) \geq \left\| \sum \lambda_i b_i \right\| - \|f\| \geq \mu \times \{\varrho + 1 + \|f\|\}/\mu - \|f\| = \varrho + 1 .$$

This completes the proof of the existence of a best approximation. Note that we have made two appeals to the fact that a continuous function defined on a bounded closed subset of an ordinary n-dimensional space attains its lower bound. This is established by a 'bisection' argument, using the fact that a contracting sequence of not-empty closed sets cannot be empty.

In the finite-dimensional case the concepts of linear transformation and matrix are all important. The definition of a linear transformation of a vector space X into a vector space Y applies equally in the infinite-dimensional case. As before the linear transformations of X into Y themselves form a vector space:

$$(L_1 + L_2)\,(x) = L_1(x) + L_2(x) ,$$

$$(c\,L)\,(x) = c\,L(x)$$

(same scalars). We say that a linear transformation is bounded if there is a constant M such that

$$\| L(x) \| \leq M \| x \| .$$

The norm on the left is that in Y and the norm on the right is that in X. The lower bound of such M is called **the** *bound* or *norm* of L and is denoted by $\| L \|$.

To clarify this concept we examine a finite dimensional case when we do not use the enclidean norm. We define, where X consists of n-tuples and Y of m-tuples of real numbers:

$$\| x \| = \max(|x_1|, |x_2|, \ldots, |x_n|), \quad \| y \| = \max(|y_1|, |y_2|, \ldots, |y_m|) .$$

A linear transformation L is specified when we know the transforms of the unit vectors ε_i in X :

$$L\,\varepsilon_i = \sum_{j=1}^{m} a_{ij}\,\eta_j , \quad i = 1, 2, \ldots, n$$

where the η_j are the unit vectors in Y. We have

$$x = \sum x_i\, \varepsilon_i \to y = \sum \sum x_i\, a_{ij}\, \eta_j = \sum_j \left(\sum_i x_i\, a_{ij}\right) \eta_j .$$

Then we have

$$\| y \| = \max\left(\left|\sum x_i\, a_{i_1}\right|, \left|\sum x_i\, a_{i_2}\right|, \ldots, \left|\sum x_i\, a_{im}\right| \right) \leq \max_{1 \leq j \leq m} \left(\sum |x_i|\,|a_{ij}|\right)$$

$$\leq \max_{1 \leq j \leq m} \left(\| x \| \sum_i |a_{ij}| \right)$$

$$\leq \| x \| \max_{1 \leq j \leq m} \sum_i |a_{ij}| .$$

Hence

$$\| L \| \leq \max_{1 \leq j \leq m} \sum_i |a_{ij}| .$$

We can show that we actually have equality, for suppose

$$\max_{1 \leq j \leq m} \sum |a_{ij}| = \sum |a_{i\hat{j}}|$$

and consider

$$x = (\operatorname{sign} a_{1\hat{j}},\ \operatorname{sign} a_{2\hat{j}},\ \ldots,\ \operatorname{sign} a_{n\hat{j}}) .$$

Then we have $\| x \| = 1$ and

$$\| y \| \geq \sum \operatorname{sign} a_{i\hat{j}}\, a_{i\hat{j}} = \sum |a_{i\hat{j}}| .$$

Hence

$$\| L \| = \max_j \sum_i |a_{ij}| .$$

A special case of a linear transformation is that of a linear functional, which maps X into R_1. The set of bounded linear functionals on a normed space X forms itself a normed (linear vector) space, called the *dual space $X*$* of X.

In certain cases it is possible to determine the form of the most general linear functional. We mention only the fact that in the Hilbert space l^2 the most general linear functional F is an inner product $F(x) = (x, f) = \sum x_i\, f_i$, and $\| F \| = \| f \|$.

We have already met linear functionals, e.g., the Lagrangian interpolant. The formulas of approximate quadrature to be discussed in Chapter 9 are also linear functionals. So also is an integral

$$I = \int_a^b f(x)\, dx .$$

Indeed the basic problem of Chapter 9, which is to find 'good' quadrature formulas $Q = \sum \lambda_i\, f(x_i)$ is a problem set in the dual space $X*$: we want to have I near Q i.e. $\| I - Q \|$ small, and we may want to compare two quadrature formulas Q_1 and Q_2, i.e., compare $\| I - Q_1 \|$ and $\| I - Q_2 \|$. See DAVIS (1963).

Todd 6

Chapter 8. Problems

8.1   Show that the best approximation in a strongly normed linear vector space is unique.

8.2   Consider a linear transformation L of one n-dimensional vector space X into another, Y. Suppose each is given the usual norm

$$\| x \| = \sqrt{\left\{ \sum_i | x_i^2 | \right\}}, \quad \| y \| = \sqrt{\left\{ \sum_i | y_i^2 | \right\}}.$$

Show that the norm of L is given by

$$\| L \| = \sqrt{\Lambda}$$

where Λ is the largest characteristic value of $A^* A$, where L is given by $y = A x$.

8.3   What are the norms of the linear functionals

$$\text{(a)} \quad Q(f) = \sum_{i=1}^n a_i f(x_i), \qquad \text{(b)} \quad I(f) = \int_a^b f(x)\, w(x)\, dx,$$

where $f(x)$ is continuous on $[a, b]$, where $x_i \in [a, b]$, $i = 1, 2, \ldots, n$, and where $w(x)$ is a non-negative weight function and where the norm is the Chebyshev norm:

$$\| f \| = \max_{a \le x \le b} | f(x) | \quad ?$$

CHAPTER 9

Approximate Quadrature

The idea of an approximate quadrature of the form

$$I = \int_a^b f(x)\, dx \doteq Q = \sum \lambda_i f(x_i)$$

is a very ancient one, and various aspects of it are covered elsewhere. As in Chapter 6, we do not intend to stress the practical aspects of this subject, but shall concentrate on some of the more theoretical aspects.

An obvious approach to this problem is the following: an approximation to the integral of a function is the integral of an approximation to the function. Application of this idea leads to Lagrangian quadratures. If

$$f(x) \doteq L_n(f, x) = \sum f(x_i)\, l_i(x) ,$$

then

$$I \doteq Q = \int_a^b \sum f(x_i)\, l_i(x)\, dx = \sum f(x_i) \int_a^b l_i(x)\, dx = \sum \lambda_i f(x_i) .$$

The error estimate (6.2), in the case of $(n + 1)$ nodes, $x_0, x_1, \ldots, x_n$, gives

$$f(x) - L_n(f, x) = [f^{(n+1)}(\zeta)/(n + 1)!]\, (x - x_0) \cdots (x - x_n)$$

and leads to

$$|I - Q| \le \frac{\max |f^{(n+1)}(x)|}{(n + 1)!} \int_a^b |(x - x_0)(x - x_1) \cdots (x - x_n)|\, dx . \qquad (9.1)$$

This result implies that any $(n + 1)$-point Lagrangian quadrature for a polynomial of degree n is exact. (Observe that this remains true for the weighted case

$$Q = \sum \lambda_i f(x_i) \doteq I = \int_a^b f(x)\, w(x)\, dx .)$$

As in Chapter 6 we can ask what is the best choice of the nodes $x_0, x_1, x_2, \ldots, x_n$? One answer to this was given by KORKINE and ZOLOTAREFF in 1873, based on the estimate (9.1):

(9.1) *The minimum value of*

$$\int_{-1}^{+1} | \tilde{p}_n(x) | \, dx \, ,$$

over all polynomials of degree n, with leading coefficient unity, is 2^{1-n} and this is attained only by $\tilde{p}_n(x) = \tilde{U}_n(x)$. Hence the Lagrangian quadrature based on the zeros of $U_n(x)$ is a best possible one.

Proof of (9.1): We shall first show that:

$$\int_{-1}^{+1} x^r \, \text{sign} \, \tilde{U}_n(x) \, dx = 0, \quad \text{if} \quad r = 0, 1, 2, \ldots, n - 1 \, , \qquad (9.2)$$

$$= 2^{1-n}, \quad \text{if} \quad r = n \, .$$

This will imply

$$\int_{-1}^{+1} \tilde{p}_n(x) \, \text{sign} \, \tilde{U}_n(x) \, dx = 2^{1-n}$$

and therefore, invariably,

$$\int_{-1}^{+1} | \tilde{p}_n(x) | \, dx \geq 2^{1-n} \, ,$$

and also that

$$\int_{-1}^{+1} | \tilde{U}_n(x) | \, dx = 2^{1-n} \, .$$

It follows that, if

$$\int_{-1}^{+1} | \tilde{p}_n(x) | \, dx = 2^{1-n} \, ,$$

we would have

$$\int_{-1}^{+1} | \tilde{p}_n(x) | \{ 1 - \text{sign} \, \tilde{p}_n(x) \, \text{sign} \, \tilde{U}_n(x) \} \, dx = 0 \, .$$

This implies [cf. **(5.2)**] that, in $(-1, 1)$,

$$\text{sign} \, \tilde{p}_n(x) \, \text{sign} \, \tilde{U}_n(x) \equiv 1 \, ,$$

so that the zeros of $\tilde{p}_n(x)$, $\tilde{U}_n(x)$ in $(-1, 1)$ must coincide. However $\tilde{U}_n$ has only simple zeros, all in $(-1, 1)$, and so therefore has $\tilde{p}_n(x)$. Since each has leading coefficient unity, we must have $\tilde{p}_n(x) \equiv \tilde{U}_n(x)$, establishing the uniqueness of the extremal polynomial.

We establish (9.2) as follows. Putting $\theta = \arccos x$ we have to evaluate

$$I_r = \int_0^\pi \cos^r \theta \; \text{sign}(\sin (n + 1) \theta / \sin \theta) \; \sin \theta \; d\theta \; .$$

We can omit the $\sin \theta$ in the argument of sign. Now

$$\text{sign}(\sin (n + 1) \theta) = (- 1)^k \quad \text{if} \quad k \pi < (n + 1) \theta < (k + 1) \pi \; .$$

Hence

$$I_r = \sum (- 1)^k \int_{k\phi}^{(k + 1)\phi} \cos^r \theta \; \sin \theta \; d\theta$$

where the summation is for $k = 0, 1, \ldots, n$ and where $\phi = \pi/(n + 1)$. Thus

$$(r + 1) I_r = \sum (- 1)^{k+1} \{\cos^{r+1} (k + 1) \phi - \cos^{r+1} k \phi\} \; .$$

The evaluation of $I_r = 2^{1-n} \delta(r, n)$ now follows from **Problems 5.9** and **5.10**. This completes the proof of **(9.1)**.

Another, earlier, answer to the question of finding 'better' quadrature formulas was given by GAUSS in 1814. In a Lagrangian quadrature, assigning the nodes determines the multipliers

$$\lambda_i = \int_a^b l_i(x) \; dx \; .$$

It is plausible that we can choose the $2n$ quantities λ_i, x_i in such a way as to satisfy the $2n$ equations

$$\int_a^b x^r \; dx = \sum \lambda_i x_i^r, \quad r = 0, 1, \ldots, 2n - 1 \; ,$$

which would imply that the quadrature is exact, i.e.,

$$\int_a^b p_{2n-1}(x) \; dx = \sum \lambda_i \; p_{2n-1}(x_i) \; ,$$

for any polynomial of degree $2n - 1$ at most. This is indeed the case, and even more is true, we can find such quadratures for any fixed positive weight function $w(x)$. Such quadratures are called Gaussian.

(9.2) Let $\{\pi_n(x)\}$ denote the polynomials orthogonal with respect to $w(x)$ on $[a, b]$. Then, if $x_i^{(n)} = x_i$ are the zeros of $\pi_n(x)$ we have

$$\int_a^b p_{2n-1}(x) \; w(x) \; dx = \sum \lambda_i \; p_{2n-1}(x_i) \; , \qquad (9.3)$$

for any polynomial $p_{2n-1}(x)$ of degree $2n - 1$, where

$$\lambda_i = \int_a^b w(x)\, l_i(x)\, dx\,, \quad l_i(x) = \frac{\pi_n(x)}{\pi_n'(x_i)\,(x - x_i)}\,. \tag{9.4}$$

Proof. We may write any $p_{2n-1}(x)$ in the form

$$p_{2n-1}(x) = q(x)\, \pi_n(x) + r(x) \tag{9.5}$$

where $q(x)$, $r(x)$ are of degree $n - 1$ at most. We then have

$$I = \int_a^b p_{2n-1}(x)\, w(x)\, dx = \int_a^b q(x)\, \pi_n(x)\, w(x)\, dx + \int_a^b r(x)\, w(x)\, dx$$

and the first integral on the right vanishes by orthogonality. Now since any n-point Lagrangian quadrature (even with an arbitrary weight) is exact for any polynomial of degree at most $n - 1$ we have, with λ_i as defined above in (9.4),

$$I = \int_a^b r(x)\, w(x)\, dx = \sum \lambda_i\, r(x_i)\,.$$

However, from (9.5), since $\pi_n(x_i) = 0$, we have $r(x_i) = p_{2n-1}(x_i)$. Hence

$$I = \sum \lambda_i\, p_{2n-1}(x_i)\,,$$

the result (9.3) required.

The converse of this is true (**Problem 9.4**).

(9.3) *The multipliers or Christoffel numbers λ_i defined in (9.4) are always positive.*

Proof. The quadrature formula (9.3) is necessarily exact for

$$f(x) = f_i(x) = \pi_n^2(x)/(x - x_i)^2$$

since this is a polynomial of degree $2n - 2$. It is clear that

$$f_i(x_j) = 0\,, \quad j = 1, 2, \ldots, n\,, \quad j \neq i\,,$$

$$f_i(x_i) = \pi_n'^2(x_i)\,.$$

Hence

$$\int_a^b \{\pi_n^2(x)/(x - x_i)^2\}\, w(x)\, dx = \lambda_i\, \pi_n'^2(x_i)$$

so that

$$\lambda_i = \int_a^b l_i^2(x)\, w(x)\, dx\,, \quad l_i = \frac{\pi_n(x)}{\pi_n'(x_i)\,(x - x_i)}\,,$$

and hence $\lambda_i > 0$, $i = 1, 2, \ldots, n$.

(9.4)   *If $f^{(2n)}(x)$ is continuous in $[a, b]$ then we have*

$$I - Q = [f^{(2n)}(\zeta)/(2\,n)\,!] \int_a^b \tilde{\pi}_n^2(x)\ w(x)\ dx \qquad (9.6)$$

for some ζ in $[a, b]$.

Proof. Let $x_1, x_2, \ldots, x_n$ be the zeros of $\pi_n(x)$. Consider the Hermite Polynomial $H(x)$ introduced in Chapter 6 which satisfies

$$H(x_i) = f(x_i)\,, \quad H'(x_i) = f'(x_i)\,, \quad i = 1, 2, \ldots, n\,.$$

We have already noted the error estimate **(6.3)**

$$f(x) - H(x) = \frac{f^{(2n)}(\zeta(x))}{(2\,n)\,!}\ (x - x_1)^2 \cdots (x - x_n)^2\,.$$

If we multiply this across by $w(x)$ and integrate between (a, b) we find

$$\int_a^b f(x)\ w(x)\ dx$$

$$= \int_a^b H(x)\ w(x)\ dx + \int_a^b \frac{f^{(2n)}(\zeta(x))}{(2\,n)\,!}\ (x - x_1)^2 \cdots (x - x_n)^2\ w(x)\ dx\,.$$

Now since $H(x)$ is of degree $2\,n - 1$, we have, exactly,

$$\int_a^b H(x)\ w(x)\ dx = \sum \lambda_i\,H(x_i) = \sum \lambda_i\,f(x_i)\,.$$

Hence

$$\int_a^b f(x)\ w(x)\ dx = \sum \lambda_i\,f(x_i) + R_n$$

where

$$R_n = \int_a^b \frac{f^{(2n)}(\zeta(x))}{(2\,n)\,!}\ (x - x_1)^2 \cdots (x - x_n)^2\ w(x)\ dx\,.$$

But

$$(x - x_1)^2 \cdots (x - x_n)^2\ w(x)/(2\,n)\,!$$

is non-negative and so the mean value theorem gives us the result (9.6) we require.

The integral in (9.6) can be calculated for any particular set of orthogonal polynomials. The results in the classical cases are given at the bottom of the relevant pages in Chapter 5.

Our last topic is that of Quadrature Schemes (cf. the Interpolation Schemes of Chapter 6). We now consider two triangular arrays, one of nodes and one of multipliers:

$$x_1^{(1)} \qquad\qquad\qquad\qquad A_1^{(1)}$$
$$x_1^{(2)} \qquad x_2^{(2)} \qquad\qquad A_1^{(2)} \qquad A_2^{(2)}$$
$$x_1^{(3)} \qquad x_2^{(3)} \qquad x_3^{(3)} \qquad A_1^{(3)} \qquad A_2^{(3)} \qquad A_3^{(3)}$$

$$\cdots \qquad\qquad\qquad\qquad \cdots$$

We consider the truth of the relation

$$Q_n(f) = \sum A_i^{(n)} f(x_i^{(n)}) \rightarrow \int_a^b f(x)\, dx . \tag{9.7}$$

Similar considerations are applicable in the weighted case. The following result is due to PÓLYA (1933) and STEKLOFF (1916).

(9.5) *In order that* (9.7) *should hold for every continuous function* $f(x)$ *it is necessary and sufficient that*

(i)   (9.7) *hold for every polynomial* $f(x)$

and

(ii) $\displaystyle\sum_{k=1}^{n} |A_k^{(n)}|$ *should be bounded.*

The most appealing proof of this depends on the ideas of Chapter 8. See, e.g., DAVIS (1963).

We note that (i) is satisfied for any Lagrangian quadrature. We note also that in the case when the $A_k^{(n)}$ are non-negative, (i) $\Rightarrow$ (ii): for if we take $f(x) \equiv 1$, $Q_n(f) \rightarrow (b - a)$ so that $Q_n(f)$ is certainly bounded but $Q_n(f) = \sum A_k^{(n)} = \sum |A_k^{(n)}|$. Combining these two observations we deduce from (**9.5**):

(9.6) *A Lagrangian quadrature scheme with non-negative multipliers is convergent for any continuous function.*

It can be proved that the multipliers corresponding to the cases when the nodes are the zeros of $T_n(x)$, or those of $U_n(x)$, are positive. This result is to be distinguished from the corresponding special case of (**9.3**).

(9.7) (STIELTJES). *The general Gaussian quadrature scheme, for any weight function* $w(x)$ *on an interval* $[a, b]$, *is convergent for any continuous function* $f(x)$.

Proof. By the Weierstrass Theorem (2.1), given any $\varepsilon > 0$, there is a polynomial $p(x) = p_\varepsilon(x)$ of degree N, say, such that $|p(x) - f(x)| < \varepsilon$, $a \le x \le b$. Then

$$|I - Q_n(f)| \le \left| \int_a^b f(x)\, w(x)\, dx - \int_a^b p(x)\, w(x)\, dx \right|$$

$$+ \left| \int_a^b p(x)\, w(x)\, dx - Q_n(p) \right| + |Q_n(p) - Q_n(f)| \,.$$

The first term on the right does not exceed

$$\varepsilon \int_a^b w(x)\, dx$$

by our choice of $p(x)$. The third term similarly does not exceed

$$\varepsilon \sum A_k^{(n)} = \varepsilon \int_a^b w(x)\, dx$$

[the last equality follows by taking $f(x) = 1$]. All this is true for any n. If we take n so that $2n - 1 \ge N$, the middle term vanishes as the quadrature is exact. Hence we have

$$|I - Q_n(f)| \le 2\varepsilon \int_a^b w(x)\, dx, \quad 2n - 1 \ge N$$

and so, ε being arbitrary,

$$I = \lim Q_n(f) \,.$$

We note the following negative result, of which we do not give the proof,

(9.8) (KUSMIN). *A Lagrangian quadrature scheme with equally spaced nodes is not convergent for every continuous function.*

We conclude by establishing an alternative representation of the weights or Christoffel numbers. This is useful in the evaluation of the λ_i in some cases when (9.4) is not convenient:

(9.9) $$\lambda_i = \frac{k_{n+1}}{k_n} \frac{-1}{\pi_{n+1}(x_i)\, \pi_n'(x_i)} \,.$$

Proof. We observe that

$$\int_a^b \sum_{r=0}^n \pi_r(x)\, \pi_r(y)\, w(x)\, dx = 1 \tag{9.8}$$

for the left hand side can be written as

$$\sum_{r=0}^{n} \pi_r(y) \int_{a}^{b} \pi_r(x)\, w(x)\, dx = \sum_{r=0}^{n} \pi_r(y)\, (1,\, \pi_r) = 1$$

since $(1,\, \pi_r) = 0$ when $r > 0$, and $(1,\, \pi_0) = 1/\pi_0$.

We now take the Christoffel-Darboux formula (**Problem 5.13**) and in it put $y = x_i$. We get, on multiplication through by $w(x)$ and integration, using (9.8):

$$1 = -\frac{k_n}{k_{n+1}} \int_{a}^{b} \frac{\pi_{n+1}(x_i)\, \pi_n(x)\, w(x)\, dx}{x - x_i}$$

which, combined with the definition of the λ_i :

$$\lambda_i = \int_{a}^{b} \frac{w(x)\, \pi_n(x)}{\pi_n'(x_i)\, (x - x_i)}\, dx .$$

gives the result required.

Chapter 9. Problems

9.1 Show that the quadrature

$$\int_1^3 f(x)\, dx = \frac{5}{9} f\left(2 - \sqrt{\frac{3}{5}}\right) + \frac{8}{9} f(2) + \frac{5}{9} f\left(2 + \sqrt{\frac{3}{5}}\right)$$

is exact when f is a polynomial of degree at most five.

Indicate how to obtain a similar result which would be exact when f is a polynomial of degree at most seven, and the integration is over an arbitrary interval $[a, b]$.

9.2 Use the expression

$$\lambda_i = -\frac{k_{n+1}}{k_n} \times \frac{1}{\pi_{n+1}(x_i)\, \pi_n'(x_i)}$$

to obtain the Christoffel numbers given at the end of Chapter 5.

9.3 Prove (**9.7**) using the last result in Chapter 6.

9.4 Establish the converse of (**9.2**), i.e., prove the following.

If $x_1, \ldots, x_n$ are points in $[a, b]$ such that

$$\int_a^b p_{2n-1}(x)\, w(x)\, dx = \sum \lambda_i\, p_{2n-1}(x_i)$$

for certain numbers λ_i, and for all polynomials $p_{2n-1}(x)$ of degree $2n-1$ at most, then $x_1, \ldots, x_n$ are the zeros of a polynomial of degree n, orthogonal to $1, x, \ldots, x^{n-1}$ over the interval $[a, b]$, with weight function $w(x)$.

9.5 (TCHAKALOFF). If $f(x)$ is a polynomial of degree $2n$ show that

$$f(b) - f(a) = (b - a)\, f'(\zeta)$$

where

$$\frac{1}{2}(a + b) - \frac{1}{2}(b - a)\, x_1 \le \zeta \le \frac{1}{2}(a + b) + \frac{1}{2}(b - a)\, x_1$$

where x_1 is the greatest zero of $P_n(x)$.

9.6 Evaluate

$$\int_{10}^{\infty} (e^{-u}/u)\, du$$

using the Laguerre quadrature, with three and five points.

9.7 (GAUTSCHI). Show that the error

$$R(f) = \int_a^b f(x)\, w(x)\, dx - \sum_{r=1}^{n} \lambda_r\, f(x_r)$$

in the Gaussian quadrature over a finite interval $[a, b]$, of a continuous function $f(x)$, satisfies

$$| R(f) | \leq 2\, \mu_0\, E_{2n-1}(f)$$

where $E_{2n-1}(f)$ is the error in the best uniform approximation to $f(x)$ on $[a, b]$ by polynomials of degree not exceeding $2\,n - 1$ and where

$$\mu_0 = \int_a^b w(x)\, dx .$$

9.8   Find the cubic $q(x) = a + b\, x + c\, x^2 + d\, x^3$ which coincides with $f(x)$ for $x = -1, 0, 1$ and, in addition, has $f'(0) = q'(0) = b$.

Evaluate

$$Q = \int_{-1}^{+1} q(x)\, dx$$

in terms of the ordinates $f(-1)$, $f(0)$, $f(1)$.

Estimate $Q - I$ where

$$I = \int_{-1}^{+1} f(x)\, dx .$$

Solutions to Problems

CHAPTER 1

1.1 Solution

$$\frac{1}{(n + x + 1)(n + x + 2)} = \frac{1}{n + x + 1} - \frac{1}{n + x + 2}.$$

Hence

$$\sum_{n=0}^{N} \frac{1}{(n + x + 1)(n + x + 2)}$$

$$= \left(\frac{1}{x + 1} - \frac{1}{x + 2}\right) + \left(\frac{1}{x + 2} - \frac{1}{x + 3}\right) + \cdots \left(\frac{1}{N + x + 1} - \frac{1}{N + x + 2}\right)$$

$$= \frac{1}{x + 1} - \frac{1}{N + x + 2}.$$

As

$$N \to \infty, \quad \sum_{n=0}^{N} \to (x + 1)^{-1}$$

and

$$R_n(x) = (n + x + 1)^{-1}.$$

If $n_0 = n_0(x)$ is the least n such that $R_n(x) < 0.05$ we find

$$n_0(10) = 10, \quad n_0(1) = 19, \quad n_0(0.1) = 19,$$

$$n_0(0.01) = 19, \quad n_0(0.001) = 19, \quad n_0(0) = 20.$$

[Draw a graph of $n_0(x)$ against x.]

1.2 Solution

$$\frac{x(x + 2)n^2 + x(4 - x)n + 1 - x}{n(n + 1)(n - 1)[(n - 1)x + 1](nx + 1)}$$

$$= \left(\frac{1}{n} - \frac{1}{n + 1}\right) + \left(\frac{2}{(n - 1)x + 1} - \frac{2}{nx + 1}\right).$$

As before

$$\sum_{n=1}^{N} = \frac{1}{1} - \frac{1}{N + 1} + \frac{2}{1} - \frac{2}{Nx + 1} = 3 - \frac{1}{N + 1} - \frac{2}{Nx + 1}.$$

Hence

$$R_n = \frac{1}{n + 1} + \frac{2}{nx + 1}$$

and we now find

$$n_0(10) = 24 , \quad n_0(1) = 60 , \quad n_0(0.1) = 411 ,$$

$$n_0(0.01) = 3921 , \quad n_0(0.001) = 39021 , \quad n_0(0) = 20 .$$

[Draw a graph of $n_0(x)$ against x.]

1.3 Solution

(1) No. (2) Yes. (3) Yes. (4) Yes. (5) Yes. (6) Yes. The answers to (5), (6) follow from (2) and (3) immediately. The answers to (1), (4) are obvious. Draw diagrams but do not use them!

(2) A polygonal function being continuous, the only difficulty is at $x = 0$. Take any $\varepsilon > 0$. Choose the least $n_0 = n(\varepsilon)$ for which $2^{-n_0} = \varepsilon_{n_0} < \varepsilon$. Since the graph of $f(x)$ lies between the x-axis and the parabola $y^2 = x$, it is clear that

$$\left| f(x) - f(0) \right| = \left| f(x) \right| < \varepsilon$$

if $0 \le x \le \varepsilon_{2n_0-1}$. This establishes continuity (to the right) at $x = 0$.

(3) We use the same idea. For any two points x', x'' in $0 \le x \le \varepsilon_{2n_0}$ we have $\left| f(x') - f(x'') \right| < \varepsilon$ because for all x, $f(x) \ge 0$, and $f(x') < \varepsilon$, $f(x'') < \varepsilon$.

Consider therefore what happens when both x', x'' are outside i.e., $x' \ge \varepsilon_{2n_0}$, $x'' \ge \varepsilon_{2n_0}$.

The slopes of the sides of the peak $P_{2n-1} Q_{2n} P_{2n+1}$ are $- 2^n$, $+ 2^{n+1}$ which increase with n, i.e., decrease as we move to the right. Thus

$$\left| f(x') - f(x'') \right| \le 2^{n_0} \left| x' - x'' \right|$$

and this will be less than ε if

$$\left| x' - x'' \right| < \varepsilon/2^{n_0}$$

which is certainly true if

$$\left| x' - x'' \right| < 2^{-n_0}/2^{n_0} = 2^{-2n_0} .$$

We conclude that

$$\left| x' - x'' \right| < \varepsilon_{2n_0} \quad \text{implies} \quad \left| f(x') - f(x'') \right| < \varepsilon \tag{1}$$

provided ε_{2n_0} is not between x', x''.

The exceptional case is easily dealt with. Suppose $\left| x' - x'' \right| < \varepsilon_{2n_0}$ and $x' < \varepsilon_{2n_0} < x''$. Then $x'' < \varepsilon_{2n_0-1}$ and the possible values of $f(x'')$ do not exceed $f(\varepsilon_{2n_0}) = \varepsilon_{n_0} < \varepsilon$; since $f(x') \ge 0$, the result (1) is true unconditionally.

1.9 Solution

$$B_n(1) \equiv 1 , \quad B_n(x) \equiv x , \quad B_n(x^2) = x^2 + x(1 - x)/n ,$$

$$B_n(x^3) = x^3 + 3 x^2(1 - x)/n + x(1 - x)(1 - 2 x)/n^2 .$$

1.10   Solution

$B_n(x)$ is clearly a polynomial of degree n at most; further x^K occurs in the terms with $k = 0, 1, \ldots, K$. The contribution from the $(k + 1)$-st term is

$$f\left(\frac{k}{n}\right)\binom{n}{k}(-1)^{K-k}\binom{n-k}{K-k}$$

$$= (-1)^{K-k} f\left(\frac{k}{n}\right) - \frac{n!}{k!\,(n-k)!} \times \frac{(n-k)!}{(K-k)!\,(n-K)!}$$

$$= (-1)^{K-k} f\left(\frac{k}{n}\right)\binom{n}{k}\frac{K!}{k!\,(K-k)!}$$

$$= \binom{n}{K}\binom{K}{k}(-1)^{K-k} f\left(\frac{k}{n}\right).$$

The result follows since

$$(-1)^K \varDelta^K f(0) = f(0) - \binom{K}{1} f\left(\frac{1}{n}\right) + \binom{K}{2} f\left(\frac{2}{n}\right) + \cdots + (-1)^K f\left(\frac{K}{n}\right).$$

Remark. This result leads to an alternative proof of BERNSTEINS' Theorem. For

$$\binom{n}{K}\varDelta^K f(0) = \frac{1}{K!}\left[1 - \frac{1}{n}\right]\left[1 - \frac{2}{n}\right]\cdots\left[1 - \frac{K-1}{n}\right]\frac{\varDelta^K f(0)}{(\varDelta x)^K}$$

and letting $n \to \infty$, with K fixed, we have

$$\binom{n}{K}\varDelta^K f(0) \to f^{(K)}(0)/K!$$

if the derivative exists. Thus, the Bernstein polynomials formally approach the Taylor expansion.

1.14   Solution

$$M_n = \operatorname*{lub}_{0 \le x < \infty}\left|\frac{1}{n+x+1}\right| = \frac{1}{n+1}.$$

1.15   Solution

$$M_n = \max\left\{\operatorname*{lub}_{0 < x < \infty}\left|\frac{1}{n+1} + \frac{2}{n\,x+1}\right|, \frac{1}{n+1}\right\} = 2 + \frac{1}{n+1}.$$

1.19   Solution

For a discussion of this finite difference analogue of ROLLE's Theorem see LEVIT (1963). It is shown that under the stated hypotheses, if n is the exact number of changes of sign of $f(x)$ in (a, b), then the conclusion follows if

$$h \le H_n = (b - a)/[(n + 3)/2],$$

and the bound H_n cannot be improved.

CHAPTER 2

2.2 Solution

We use the fact that

$$2^{2n-1} \cos^{2n} \frac{1}{2} \alpha = \cos n\,\alpha + 2\,n \cos(n-1)\,\alpha$$

$$+ \frac{1}{2}(2\,n)(2\,n-1)\cos(n-2)\,\alpha + \cdots + \frac{1}{2}(2\,n)\,!/(n\,!)^2 \,.$$

This is easily established by induction using properties of the binomial coefficients. Alternatively, using complex numbers, we let $x = \cos\theta + i \sin\theta$ so that $x^{-1} = \cos\theta - i\sin\theta$ and thus $x + x^{-1} = 2\cos\theta$. Hence $2^{2n}\cos^{2n}\theta = (x + x^{-1})^{2n} = (x^{2n} + x^{-2n}) + 2\,n(x^{2n-2} + x^{-2n+2}) + \cdots + (2\,n!)/(n!)^2$, by the binomial series, collecting terms in pairs from front and back. Now, by DEMOIVRE's Theorem $x^r + x^{-r} = (\cos r\,\theta + i\sin r\,\theta) + (\cos r\,\theta - i\sin r\,\theta) = 2\cos r\,\theta$. The result follows by dividing across by 2 and putting $\alpha/2 = \theta$.

Substituting this result in the integrand we find

$$\frac{2^{2n}(2\,n-1)\,!!}{(2\,n)\,!!} V_n(F,\theta) = \frac{1}{\pi} \int_{-\pi}^{+\pi} F(\phi) \left\{ \frac{1}{2} \frac{(2\,n)\,!}{(n\,!)^2} + \sum_{r=1}^{n} \binom{2\,n}{n+r} \cos r(\theta-\phi) \right\} d\phi$$

$$= \frac{1}{2} \frac{2\,n!}{(n\,!)^2} \frac{1}{\pi} \int_{-\pi}^{+\pi} F(\phi)\,d\phi$$

$$+ \sum_{r=1}^{n} \binom{2\,n}{n+r} \left\{ \cos r\theta \frac{1}{\pi} \int_{-\pi}^{+\pi} F(\phi)\cos r\,\phi\,d\phi + \sin r\theta \frac{1}{\pi} \int_{-\pi}^{+\pi} F(\phi)\sin r\,\phi\,d\phi \right\}$$

$$= \frac{2\,n!}{(n\,!)^2} \frac{1}{2} A_0 + \sum_{r=1}^{n} \binom{2\,n}{n+r} (A_r \cos r\,\theta + B_r \sin r\,\theta) \,.$$

Thus the ratios required are

$$\binom{2\,n}{n+r} \frac{(2\,n)\,!!}{2^{2n}(2\,n-1)\,!!} = \frac{(n\,!)^2}{(n+r)\,!\,(n-r)\,!} \,.$$

2.3 Solution

The rate of convergence of $B_n(e^x, x)$ can be estimated in an elementary way as follows. Write $E_n(x) = [1 + x(e^{1/n} - 1)]^n - e^x$. Observe that

$$[1 + x(e^{1/n} - 1)] - e^{x/n} = \frac{x}{2\,!\,n^2} + \frac{x}{3\,!\,n^3} + \cdots$$

$$- \frac{x^2}{2\,!\,n^2} - \frac{x^3}{3\,!\,n^3} - \cdots$$

and so, if $0 \le x \le 1$,

$$0 \le 1 + x(e^{1/n} - 1) - e^{x/n} \le \frac{x}{n^2} \left\{ \frac{1}{2\,!} + \frac{1}{3\,!} + \cdots \right\} = \frac{x}{n^2} \{e - 2\} \,.$$

Next we use the fact that if $a \geq b$

$$a^n - b^n = (a - b)(a^{n-1} + \cdots + b^{n-1}) \leq (a - b) n a^{n-1}$$

with $a = 1 + x(e^{1/n} - 1)$, $b = e^{x/n}$. This gives

$$0 \leq E_n(x) \leq \frac{x}{n^2} (e - 2) n[1 + x(e^{1/n} - 1)]^{n-1}.$$

The last factor does not exceed $e^{(e-1)}$ since

$$x(e^{1/n} - 1) = x \left[\frac{1}{n} + \frac{1}{2! \, n^2} + \cdots \right]$$

$$\leq \frac{x}{n} \left[1 + \frac{1}{2! \, n} + \frac{1}{3! \, n^2} + \cdots \right]$$

$$\leq \frac{x}{n} \left[1 + \frac{1}{2!} + \frac{1}{3!} + \cdots \right] = \frac{x}{n} (e - 1)$$

and since $(1 + y/n)^n$ increases to its limit e^y, y being positive. Hence we have

$$0 \leq E_n(x) \leq \frac{x}{n} (e - 2) e^{(e-1) x},$$

i.e.,

$$E_n(x) = O\left(\frac{1}{n}\right).$$

2.4 Solution

We write $[x]$ for the integral part of x. Then the polynomials

$$p_n(x) = \sum_{k=0}^{n} \left[\binom{n}{k} f\left(\frac{k}{n}\right) \right] x^k (1 - x)^{n-k}$$

all have integral coefficients. Further,

$$\left| B_n(f, x) - p_n(x) \right| \leq |f(1)| \, x^n + \sum_{k=1}^{n-1} x^k (1 - x)^{n-k} + (1 - x)^n |f(0)|.$$

If $0 < a \leq x \leq b < 1$, and if M is an upper bound for $|f(x)|$ in $[0, 1]$ we have

$$\left| B_n(f, x) - p_n(x) \right| \leq M \{b^n + (1 - a)^n\} + \frac{1}{n} \sum_{k=1}^{n-1} \binom{n}{k} x^k (1 - x)^{n-k}$$

$$\leq M \{b^n + (1 - a)^n\} + \frac{1}{n} \sum_{0}^{n} \binom{n}{k} x^k (1 - x)^{n-k}$$

$$= M \{b^n + (1 - a)^n\} + \frac{1}{n}$$

and this tends uniformly to zero. The conclusion follows.

2.8 Solution

$$B_n(f, x).$$

CHAPTER 3

3.1   Solution

See NATIONAL BUREAU OF STANDARDS (1952).

3.3   Solution

See JONES et al. (1946) or JAHNKE-EMDE-LÖSCH (1960).

3.4   Solution

See NATIONAL BUREAU OF STANDARDS (1952).

3.10   Solution

$$T_n\big((2\,x - 1)\cos\pi/2\,n\big) = 2^{n-1}\,(2\cos\pi/2\,n)^n\,x^n + \cdots$$
$$= a_n[x^n + \cdots] = a_n\,p_n(x)\,,$$

say, where $a_n = 2^{n-1}(2\cos\pi/2\,n)^n$.

We have $\quad p_n(0) = a_n^{-1}\,T_n(-\cos\pi/2\,n) = a_n^{-1}\left(\cos\left(-\pi/2\right)\right) = 0 \quad$ and $p_n(1) = a_n^{-1}\,T_n(\cos\pi/2\,n) = a_n^{-1}\left(\cos\left(\pi/2\right)\right) = 0.$

Since $T_n(x)$ has $n - 1$ extrema interior to $[-1, 1]$, $p_n(x)$ will have $n - 1$ extrema interior to $[0, 1]$ and the values assumed at these will be $\pm a_n^{-1}$, alternately. Suppose that there was another polynomial q_n, with leading coefficient unity and such $q_n(0) = q_n(1) = 0$, which had

$$\max_{0 \le x \le 1}\left|\,q_n(x)\,\right| < a_n^{-1}\,.$$

Then the polynomial

$$r(x) = p_n(x) - q_n(x)$$

has degree $n - 1$ at most, and by the usual argument, has the sign of $p_n(x)$ at the extrema of $p_n(x)$, i.e., it has alternate signs at these $n - 1$-points. It follows that $r(x)$ has $n - 2$ interior zeros but also $r(0) = r(1) = 0$. Hence $r(x)$ has n zeros and is therefore identically zero.

3.12   Solution   [Cf. LANCZOS (1938)].

$$\sqrt{2}\left\{\frac{1}{2} - c\,T_1^*(x) + c^2\,T_2^*(x) - c^3\,T_3^*(x) + \cdots\right\}$$

$$= \sqrt{2}\,\mathscr{R}\left\{-\frac{1}{2} + (1 - c\,e^{i\theta} + c^2\,e^{2i\theta} - \cdots)\right\} \quad \text{if} \quad \theta = \arccos\left(2\,x - 1\right)$$

$$= \sqrt{2}\,\mathscr{R}\left\{-\frac{1}{2} + (1 + c\,e^{i\theta})^{-1}\right\}$$

$$= \sqrt{2}\left\{\frac{1}{2} - \frac{1}{2}\,c^2\right\}\{1 + 2\,c\cos\theta + c^2\}^{-1}$$

$$= \frac{2}{3 + \cos\theta}$$

$$= \frac{1}{1 + x}\,.$$

The absolute value of the error committed by taking only the first $(n + 1)$ terms in this expansion does not exceed

$$\sqrt{2} \, c^{n+1} \, \big| \{T_{n+1}(x) - c \, T_{n+2}(x) + \cdots\} \big|$$
$$\leq \sqrt{2} \, c^{n+1} \, [1 + c + c^2 + \cdots]$$
$$= \sqrt{2} \, c^{n+1}/(1 - c) \, .$$

If we take $n = 6$ we have, in $0 \leq x \leq 1$

$$\left| (1 + x)^{-1} - \left\{ \sqrt{2} \left(\tfrac{1}{2} - c \, T_1(x) + \cdots + c^6 \, T_6(x) \right) \right\} \right| \leq 7.5 \times 10^{-6} \, .$$

The numerical values of the polynomial $\{\cdots\}$ can be obtained easily—giving about a 5 decimal approximation to $(1 + x)^{-1}$. It is interesting to compare this approximation with that obtained by straight use of the power series: the number of terms required to compete with the above expansion depends on the range, the error being $x^n/(1 + x)$:

$$|x| \leq 0.1, 8; \quad |x| \leq 0.5, 17; \quad |x| \leq 0.8, 53; \quad |x| \leq 0.9, 114 \, .$$

Another comparison which is relevant is that given by the Bernstein polynomials. According to (2.5) the error is of the order of n^{-1} so that the order of 10^5 terms would be needed.

Remark. The efficiency of the approximation given by the truncated Chebyshev expansion is very remarkable. It is not, however, the best. Cf. **Problem 3.23** below.

3.14 Solution

We have to choose a, b so that

$$\max_{-1 \leq x \leq 1} \big| a \, x^2 + b \, x + 1 \big|$$

is least. Clearly $a \, x^2 + b \, x + 1 = 1$ for $x = 0$, for all a, b. Thus 1 is the least possible value and it is attained, e.g. with $a = b = 0$; it is also attained for $a = -2, b = 0$ when

$$a \, x^2 + b \, x + 1 = - T_2(x) \, .$$

3.15* Solution

For $x = \pm 1$, we have $a \, x^2 + x + b = a \pm 1 + b$. These values differ by 2, no matter what a, b are. Hence the range of variation of $a \, x^2 + x + b$ cannot be less than 2 and so the least deviation cannot be less than unity which occurs when $a + b = 0$. Now if $a = b = 0$, this value of unity is attained. Hence

$$a \, x^2 + x + b \equiv x = T_1(x)$$

is a polynomial required; the general solution is $a \, x^2 + x - a, \, |a| \leq 1/2$.

---

* Cf. p. 100.

3.16* Solution

Consider the deviations of $x^2 + a\,x + b$. Since this has values $1 \pm a + b$ at $x = \pm 1$ and b at $x = 0$, the spread of its values is at least $1 \pm a$, and so this will always exceed 1 (and the deviation will exceed 1/2), unless $a = 0$. Comparing the values at $x = \pm a$ and at 0 we see that the spread is from $1 + b$ to b and this deviation will exceed 1/2 unless $b = -1/2$. Hence $x^2 - 1/2$ attains the minimum deviation, 1/2.

3.17 Solution

M_∞ (1) Best constant is $3/4 = 0.75$: error $1/4 = 0.25$.

(2) Since $(x^{-1})'' = 2\,x^{-3}$ is of constant sign we can apply the results of pages 29-30

$$(x^{-1})' = -x^{-2} = -\frac{1}{2}\,, \quad c = \sqrt{2}$$

$$A = -\frac{1}{2}\,, \quad B = \frac{1}{2}\left[1 + \left(\frac{1}{\sqrt{2}}\right)\right] - \frac{1}{2}\left[1 + \sqrt{2}\right]\left(-\frac{1}{2}\right)$$

$$= 3/4 + \frac{1}{\sqrt{2}} = 1.4571\,.$$

Error $= 0.0429$.

M_2 (1) $E_0^2 = \displaystyle\int_1^2 (x^{-1} - A)^2\,dx = A^2 - 2\,A\,\log 2 + \frac{1}{2}\,.$

$\dfrac{\partial E_0^2}{\partial A} = 0$ gives $A = \log 2$ and $E_0^2 = \dfrac{1}{2} - (\log 2)^2 = 0.0195\,.$

(2) $E_1^2 = \displaystyle\int_1^2 (x^{-1} - A\,x - B)^2\,dx$

$$= \frac{7}{3}\,A^2 + 3\,A\,B + B^2 - 2\,A - 2\,\log 2\,B + \frac{1}{2}\,.$$

$$\left.\begin{array}{l} \dfrac{\partial E_1^2}{\partial A} = \dfrac{14}{3}\,A + 3\,B - 2 = 0 \\[2mm] \dfrac{\partial E_1^2}{\partial B} = 3\,A + 2\,B - 2\,\log 2 = 0 \end{array}\right\} \text{giving} \left\{\begin{array}{l} A = 12 - 18\,\log 2 = -0.4767 \\[2mm] B = 28\,\log 2 - 18 = 1.4081\,, \end{array}\right.$$

and so

$$E_1^2 = \frac{1}{2} - A - B\,\log 2 = 0.0007\,.$$

Remark. These results are special cases of results of W. A. MARKOFF concerning the polynomials of least deviation when a particular coefficient, not the leading one, is fixed (see MUNCH [1960]). The extremal polynomials are again essentially the $T_n(x)$.

ZOLOTAREFF studied the polynomials of the form $x^n - \sigma\,x^{n-1} + p_{n-2}(x)$ of least deviation, σ being fixed.

ACHIESER and others have studied polynomials of the form $x^n - \sigma\,x^{n-1} + \tau\,x^{n-2} + p_{n-3}(x)$ of least deviation, where σ, τ are fixed. Recently MEIMAN has considered the general case when $r < n$ coefficients are fixed.

3.18 Solution

M_∞ (1) Best constant is $\frac{1}{2}$: error $\frac{9}{2}$.

(2) Since $(10^x)'' = M^{-2} 10^x$ is of constant sign we can apply the results following (**3.7**). Here

$$M = \log_{10}e = (\log_e 10)^{-1} = 0.4343 .$$

$$M^{-1} 10^c = 9 , \quad c = \log_{10}(9\,M) = 0.5920 ,$$

$$A = 9, \quad B = (1 + 9\,M) - \frac{1}{2}\,[0 + \log_{10}(9\,M)] \times 9$$

$$= (1 + 9\,M) - \frac{9\log_{10}(9\,M)}{2} = 2.5946 .$$

$$\text{Error} = 1.5946 .$$

M_2 (1) $E_0^2 = \displaystyle\int_0^1 (10^x - A)^2\,dx = A^2 - 18\,A\,M + 99\,M/2 .$

$$\frac{\partial E_0^2}{\partial A} = 2\,A - 18\,M \quad \text{gives} \quad A = 9\,M = 3.9086 \quad \text{and}$$

$$E_0^2 = M\,(99/2) - 81\,M = 6.2200 .$$

(2) $E_1^2 = \displaystyle\int_0^1 (10^x - A\,x - B)^2\,dx$

$$= \frac{A^2}{3} + A\,B + B^2 - 2\,A\,\{10\,M - 9\,M^2\} - 18\,B\,M + 99\,M/2 .$$

$$\left.\begin{array}{l}\dfrac{\partial E_1^2}{\partial A} = \dfrac{2\,A}{3} + B - 2\,(10\,M - 9\,M^2) = 0 \\[2mm] \dfrac{\partial E_1^2}{\partial B} = A + 2\,B - 18\,M = 0\end{array}\right| \begin{array}{l}\text{giving:} \\[1mm] A = 66\,M - 108\,M^2 = 8.2934 \\[1mm] B = -24\,M + 54\,M^2 = -0.2380\end{array}$$

and so $E_1^2 = 0.4882$.

3.19 Solution

We observe that

$$(\arctan x)'' = -\frac{2\,x}{(1 + x^2)^2}$$

is of constant sign in $[0,1]$.

(i) $\qquad\qquad\qquad \arctan 0 = 0 , \quad \arctan 1 = \frac{\pi}{4} .$

Best constant is therefore $(\pi/8) = 0.3927$.

(ii) $$\frac{f(b) - f(a)}{b - a} = \frac{\pi}{4}, \quad A = \frac{\pi}{4} = 0.7854 .$$

$$f'(c) = \frac{1}{1 + c^2} = \frac{\pi}{4}, \quad c^2 = \frac{4}{\pi} - 1 = 0.2732 , \quad c = 0.5227 ;$$

$$B = \frac{1}{2} \, [0 + \arctan 0.5227] - \frac{1}{2} \, (0 + 0.5227) \left(\frac{\pi}{4}\right)$$

$$= 0.2408 - 0.2053 = 0.0355 .$$

Best linear approximation is $\arctan x = 0.7854 \, x + 0.0355$.

3.22   Solution

$$\frac{1}{4} + \frac{1}{2} \sqrt{2} - \frac{1}{2} \, x = 0.9571 - 0.5 \, x$$

is the best linear approximation. The error is $(c/4) = 0.0439$ compared with 0.0503 given by the truncated Chebyshev expansion.

3.23   Solution   [Cf. HORNECKER (1958) and ACHIESER (1953); the idea goes back to CHEBYSHEV].

Using the methods of **Problem 3.12** or otherwise, we find

$$\pi_n(x) = \sqrt{2} \left\{ \frac{1/2 \, (1 - c^2) - (- 1)^n \, c^n [\cos n\, \theta + c \cos (n - 1) \, \theta]}{1 + c^2 + 2 \, c \cos \theta} + (- 1)^n \, \frac{c^n \cos n\, \theta}{(1 - c^2)} \right\}.$$

Also

$$\frac{1}{1 + x} = \frac{2}{3 + \cos \theta} .$$

Hence

$$\left\{ \frac{1}{1 + x} - \pi_n(x) \right\}$$

$$= \frac{(- 1)^n \sqrt{2} \, c^n}{2 \, c \, (3 + \cos \theta)} \, [\cos n\, \theta + \cos (n - 1) \, \theta] - (- 1)^n \, \frac{c^{n-1} \cos n\, \theta}{4}$$

$$= \frac{(- 1)^n \, c^{n-1}}{4 \sqrt{2} \, (3 + \cos \theta)} \, [4 \cos n\, \theta + 4 \, c \cos (n - 1) \, \theta - 3 \sqrt{2} \cos n\, \theta - \sqrt{2} \cos \theta \cos n\, \theta]$$

$$= \frac{(- 1)^{n-1} \, c^n}{4} \times \left\{ \frac{\cos (n + 1) \, \theta + 2 \, c \cos n\, \theta + c^2 \cos (n - 1) \, \theta}{1 + 2 \, c \cos \theta + c^2} \right\} .$$

We now consider the factor $f(\theta)$ in $\{\cdots\}$ in the last equation and show that it assumes the values ± 1, alternately for $(n + 2)$ values of θ, $0 \le \theta \le \pi$; in particular, $f(0) = 1$, $f(\pi) = (- 1)^{n+1}$. It then follows, from our fundamental theorem, that $\pi_n(x)$ is indeed the polynomial of best approximation required.

The result we need can be established by elementary trigonometry. For, it is easy to verify that

$$\frac{\cos(n+1)\theta + 2c\cos n\theta + c^2\cos(n-1)\theta}{1 + 2c\cos\theta + c^2} = \cos(n\theta + \phi)$$

where

$$\cos\phi = \frac{3\cos\theta + 1}{3 + \cos\theta}, \qquad \sin\phi = \frac{2\sqrt{2}\sin\theta}{3 + \cos\theta}.$$

Observe that ϕ is a function of θ. We note that as x goes from 0 to 1, $2x - 1$ goes from -1 to 1, and θ from π to 0, ϕ also goes from π to 0. Hence as x goes from 0 to 1, $\cos(n\theta + \phi)$ goes from $\cos(n+1)\pi$ to $\cos 0$ and there has $n + 2$ extrema, alternately ± 1.

It follows from the Chebyshev theorem that $\pi_n(x)$ is indeed the best approximation of degree n, and the error is

$$E_n = \frac{1}{4}c^n.$$

We observe that the value of the deviation $\{(x+1)^{-1} - \pi_n(x)\}$ does not exceed $c^n/4$, and that the extremal polynomial of degree n is got by taking the truncated Chebyshev expansion and dividing the term involving $T_n(x)$ by $(1 - c^2)$.

Thus for $n = 6$, the best polynomial gives an error of $1/4\,c^6 \doteqdot 6.4 \times 10^{-6}$; the estimate given for the error caused by a straight truncation was seen to be $\sqrt{2}\,c^7/(1 - c) \doteqdot 7.5 \times 10^{-6}$.

The actual value of $\pi_6(x)$ is:

$$0.9999936 - 0.9992989\,x + 0.9872992\,x^2 - 0.9110037\,x^3$$

$$+ 0.6829260\,x^4 - 0.3360329\,x^5 + 0.0761261\,x^6.$$

3.25 Solution

$$T_4(x) = 128\,x^4 - 256\,x^3 + 160\,x^2 - 32\,x + 1$$

is such that

$$|T_4(x)| \le 1, \quad 0 \le x \le 1.$$

Hence, up to an error of $1/128$ we have

$$x^4 = 2\,x^3 - \frac{5}{4}\,x^2 + \frac{1}{4}\,x - \frac{1}{128}, \quad 0 \le x \le 1.$$

Similarly, considering $T_3(x) = 32\,x^3 - 48\,x^2 + 18\,x - 1$ we see that, up to an error of $1/16$, we have

$$2\,x^3 = 3\,x^2 - \frac{9}{8}\,x + 1/16, \quad 0 \le x \le 1.$$

Combining these results we see that, up to an error of $9/128$,

$$x^4 = \frac{7}{4}\,x^2 - \frac{7}{4}\,x + \frac{7}{28}, \quad 0 \le x \le 1.$$

This process is called 'economization'.

For applications to practical problems of interpolation see e.g. CLENSHAW and OLVER (1955), CLENSHAW (1962), NAUTICAL ALMANAC OFFICE (1956).

3.28 Solution

LEGENDRE: $\dfrac{1}{2}$, $\dfrac{3}{16}$ $(5\,x^2 + 1)$, $\dfrac{15}{128}$ $(-7\,x^4 + 14\,x^2 + 1)$.

CHEBYSHEV, T_n: $\dfrac{2}{\pi}$, $\dfrac{2}{3\pi}$ $(4\,x^2 + 1)$, $\dfrac{3}{15\pi}$ $(-16\,x^4 + 36\,x^2 + 3)$.

CHEBYSHEV, U_n: $\dfrac{4}{3\pi}$, $\dfrac{8}{15\pi}$ $(6\,x^2 + 1)$, $\dfrac{4}{105\pi}$ $(-80\,x^4 + 144\,x^2 + 9)$.

BERNSTEIN: 1 , $(x^2 + 1)/2$, $(-x^4 + 6\,x^2 + 3)/8$.

3.29 Solution [Cf. VISSER (1945)].

Write $\zeta = \exp(2\,\pi\,i/n)$. Then we find, summing geometric series, that

$$\sum_{l=0}^{n-1} f(z\,\zeta^l) = n\,a_0 + n\,a_n\,z^n .$$

For some z_0, with $|z_0| = 1$, we have

$$n\,a_0 + n\,a_n\,z_0^n = n\big(|a_0| + |a_n|\big)e^{i\alpha} .$$

Hence

$$\sum_{l=0}^{n-1} f(z_0\,\zeta^l) = n\,\big(|a_0| + |a_n|\big)e^{i\alpha} \tag{1}$$

and so

$$\max_{|z|=1} |f(z)| \geq \max_{0 \leq l \leq n-1} |f(z_0\,\zeta^l)| \geq |a_0| + |a_n| . \tag{2}$$

The result required now follows using the Maximum Modulus Principle. The equality situation can be discussed as follows. Suppose

$$\max_{|z| \leq 1} |f(z)| = |a_0| + |a_n| .$$

From (2) it follows that

$$\max_{0 \leq l \leq n-1} |f(z_0\,\zeta^l)| = |a_0| + |a_n|$$

and then, using (1), we find

$$f(z_0\,\zeta^l) = a_0 + a_n\,z_0^n , \quad l = 0, 1, 2, \ldots, n-1 .$$

This gives

$$z_0^{-1}\,[f(z_0\,\zeta^l) - a_0] = a_n\,z_0^{n-1} , \quad l = 0, 1, 2, \ldots, n-1$$

and so

$$a_1 = \cdots = a_{n-1} = 0 .$$

CHAPTER 4

4.1 Solution

We use the Sonine-Pólya Theorem: If y satisfies the differential equation $\{k(x)\,y'\}' + \phi(x)\,y = 0$ where $k(x) > 0$, $\phi(x) > 0$, and both $k(x), \phi(x)$ have continuous derivatives then the relative maxima of $|\,y\,|$ in an interval $[x_0, X_0]$ form an increasing or decreasing sequence according as $k(x)\,\phi(x)$ is increasing or decreasing there. See, e.g., SZEGÖ (1939).

We prove only the special case when $k(x) \equiv 1$. Consider

$$f(x) = \{y(x)\}^2 + \psi(x)\,\{y'(x)\}^2$$

where $\psi(x) = 1/\phi(x)$. We have

$$f(x) = \{y(x)\}^2 \quad \text{if} \quad y'(x) = 0$$

and

$$f'(x) = 2\,y\,y' + 2\,\psi\,y'\,y'' + y'^2\,\psi' = y'^2\,\psi' \,,$$

since the first two terms are zero on account of the differential equation. Hence sign $f'(x) = -\,\text{sign}\,\phi'(x)$ and the result required is clear.

To apply this we note that $P_n'(x)$ satisfies the differential equation

$$[(1 - x^2)^2\,y']' + (n^2 + n - 2)\,(1 - x^2)\,y = 0\,.$$

4.3 Solution

Let $\phi \to 0$.

4.4 Solution [Cf. VISSER (1945)].

Take any z_0 with $|\,z_0\,| = 1$ and any real ϕ. Then

$$S(\phi) = \frac{f(z_0\,e^{i\phi}) - f(z_0\,e^{-i\phi})}{2\,i} = \sum_{r=1}^{n} b_r\,z_0^r\,\sin r\,\theta$$

satisfies $|\,s(\phi)\,| \leq 1$. Hence, using the result of the previous problem,

$$\left|\,b_1\,z_0 + 2\,b_2\,z_0^2 + \cdots + n\,b_n\,z_0^n\,\right| \leq n$$

i.e.,

$$\left|\,z_0\,f'(z_0)\,\right| \leq n\,;$$

since z_0 is any number with modulus 1, the result follows.

CHAPTER 5

5.2 Solution

Since $|\sin x|$ is even all the b_n are zero. We have

$$a_n = \frac{1}{\pi} \int_{-\pi}^{+\pi} |\sin x| \cos nx \, dx$$

$$= \frac{1}{\pi} \left[\int_{0}^{\pi} \sin x \cos nx \, dx - \int_{-\pi}^{0} \sin x \cos nx \, dx \right]$$

$$= \frac{2}{\pi} \int_{0}^{\pi} \sin x \cos nx \, dx$$

$$= \frac{1}{\pi} \int_{0}^{\pi} [\sin (n+1) x - \sin (n-1) x] \, dx$$

$$= \frac{1}{\pi} \left[-\frac{\cos (n+1) x}{n+1} + \frac{\cos (n-1) x}{n-1} \right]_{0}^{\pi}, \quad n \neq 1$$

$$= \frac{1}{\pi} \left[\frac{1}{n+1} \left\{ 1 - (-1)^{n+1} \right\} + \frac{1}{n-1} \left\{ -1 + (-1)^{n-1} \right\} \right]$$

$$= \begin{cases} 0 & n \quad \text{odd} \\ \dfrac{2}{\pi} \left(\dfrac{1}{n+1} - \dfrac{1}{n-1} \right) = \dfrac{-4}{\pi (n^2-1)} & n \quad \text{even.} \end{cases}$$

For

$$n = 1, \quad a_n = \frac{1}{\pi} \int_{0}^{\pi} \sin 2x \, dx = 0.$$

Hence

$$|\sin x| \sim \frac{2}{\pi} - \frac{4}{\pi} \sum_{n=1}^{\infty} \frac{\cos 2nx}{4 n^2 - 1}.$$

5.5 Solution

Assume

$$|x| = \sum_{0}^{\infty} a_i P_i(x)$$

Then remembering that $P_{2r}(x)$ is even and $P_{2r+1}(x)$ is odd it is clear that $a_1 = a_3 = \cdots = 0$. We have

$$a_{2n} \int_{-1}^{+1} P_{2n}^2(x) \, dx = \int_{-1}^{+1} |x| P_{2n}(x) \, dx = 2 \int_{0}^{1} x P_{2n}(x) \, dx$$

so that

$$a_{2n} = (4\,n + 1) \int_0^1 x\,P_{2n}(x)\,dx\ .$$

We can show

$$a_0 = \frac{1}{2}\ ,\quad a_{2n} = (-\,1)^{n+1}\,\frac{(2\,n - 2)\,!}{(n - 1)\,!\,(n + 1)\,!}\ ,\quad \frac{4\,n + 1}{2^{2n}}\ ,\quad n = 1, 2, \ldots\ (2)$$

so that

$$a_2 = 5/8\ ,\quad a_4 = -\,3/16\ ,\quad a_6 = 13/128\ , \ldots\ .$$

giving as the first approximations to $|\,x\,|$:

$$1/2\ ,\quad 3\,(5\,x^2 + 1)/16\ ,\quad 15\,(-\,7\,x^4 + 14\,x^2 + 1)/128\ , \ldots\ .$$

An elegant way of obtaining (2) (and more) is the following: Consider for arbitrary real $p > 0$

$$\int_0^1 x^p\,P_{2n}(x)\,dx\ .$$

Writing $P_{2n}(x) = k_{2n}\,x^{2n} + k_{2n-2}\,x^{2n-2} + \cdots$ we find

$$I = \int_0^1 x^p\,P_{2n}(x)\,dx = k_{2n}/(2\,n + p + 1) + k_{2n-2}/(2\,n + p - 1) + \cdots\ .$$

If we bring the right hand side to the common denominator

$$(2\,n + p + 1)\,(2\,n + p - 1)\cdots(p + 1)$$

we observe that the numerator is a polynomial of degree n in p

$$(k_{2n} + k_{2n-2} + \cdots)\,p^n + \cdots$$

and that the coefficient of p^n is $(k_{2n} + k_{2n-2} + \cdots) = P_{2n}(1) = 1$. Further, by orthogonality, the integral I vanishes for even p less than $2\,n$, i.e., for $p = 2\,n - 2, 2\,n - 4, \ldots, 2, 0$. Hence the numerator must be

$$\{p - (2\,n - 2)\}\,\{p - (2\,n - 4)\}\cdots\{p + 2\}\,p\ .$$

This gives us the integral I explicitly. [A similar argument applies to the integral

$$\int_0^1 x^p\,P_{2n+1}(x)\,dx\ .]$$

In the case $p = 1$ we have

$$\int_0^1 x \, P_{2n}(x) \, dx = \frac{\{1 - (2\,n - 2)\}\{1 - (2\,n - 4)\} \cdots \{-1\}\{1\}}{\{2\,n + 2\}\{2\,n\} \cdots \{2\}}$$

$$= (-1)^{n+1} \frac{(2\,n - 2)\,!}{2^{2n}(n + 1)\,!\,(n - 1)\,!}$$

which gives the result (2) above.

5.6　Solution

(i)　Consider

$$I_r = \int_0^\infty x^r \, e^{-x} \, dx \,.$$

Then

$$I_r = [-x^r \, e^{-x}]_0^\infty + \int_0^\infty r \, x^{r-1} \, e^{-x} \, dx = r \, I_{r-1} \,.$$

Hence

$$I_r = r \, I_{r-1} = r(r - 1) \, I_{r-2} = \cdots = r\,! \, I_0$$

where

$$I_0 = \int_0^\infty e^{-x} \, dx = [-e^{-x}]_0^\infty = 1 \,.$$

Thus $I_r = r\,!$ and so

$$\mu_n = (m + n)\,! \,.$$

(ii)

$$\int_c^d x^m \, e^{-x} \, dx \geq (d - c) \, c^m \, e^{-d} \,.$$

(iii)　By LEIBNIZ' Theorem

$$D^n[e^{-x} \, x^{m+n}] = (-1)^n \, e^{-x} \left[x^{m+n} - \binom{n}{1}(m + n) \, x^{m+n-1} \right.$$

$$+ \binom{n}{2}(m + n)(m + n - 1) \, x^{m+n-2} + \cdots$$

$$\left. + (-1)^n \binom{n}{n}(m + n)(m + n - 1) \cdots (m + 1) \, x^m \right] \,.$$

Hence

$$L_n^{(m)}(x) = (-1)^n \left[x^n - \binom{n}{1}(m + n) \, x^{n-1} + \cdots + (-1)^n (m + n)\,!/m\,! \right] / n\,! \,.$$

Thus

$$k_n = (-1)^n/n!, \quad k_n' = (-1)^{n-1}(m+n)/(n-1)!.$$

(iv)   Suppose first that $r < s$: Then integrating by parts:

$$I_{r,s} = \int_0^\infty L_r^{(m)}(x)\, L_s^{(m)}(x)\, e^{-x}\, x^m\, dx$$

$$= \int_0^\infty L_r^{(m)}(x)\, D^s[e^{-x}\, x^{m+s}]\, dx/s!$$

$$= [D^{s-1}\, [e^{-x}\, x^{m+s}]\, L_r^m(x)/s!]_0^\infty - \int_0^\infty D\,[L_r^{(m)}(x)] \times D^{s-1}\,[e^{-x}\, x^{m+s}]\, dx/s!.$$

The integrated part vanishes at $x = \infty$ because of the factor e^{-x} and at $x = 0$ because there is a factor of at least x^m in each term. Hence

$$I_{r,s} = -\int_0^\infty D\,[L_r^{(m)}(x)] \times D^{s-1}\,[e^{-x}\, x^{m+s}]\, dx/s!.$$

Repetition of this integration by parts gives

$$I_{r,s} = (-1)^{r+1}\int_0^\infty D^{r+1}\,[L_r^{(m)}(x)] \times D^{s-r-1}\,[e^{-x}\, x^{m+s}]\, dx/s!.$$

Since $L_r^{(m)}(x)$ is a polynomial of degree r, its $(r+1)$st derivative is zero. Hence $I_{r,s} = 0$ for $r < s$. This establishes orthogonality.

(v)   Whenever $r = s$ the same reasoning gives

$$I_{s,s} = (-1)^s\int_0^\infty D^s\,[L_s^{(m)}(x)] \times [e^{-x}\, x^{(m+s)}]\, dx/s!.$$

Now since

$$L_s^{(m)}(x) = [(-1)^s/s!]\, x^s + \cdots$$

we have

$$D^s\,[L_s^{(m)}(x)] = (-1)^s$$

and so

$$I_{s,s} = (-1)^s\int_0^\infty (-1)^s \times e^{-x}\, x^{(m+s)}\, dx/s! = (m+s)/s!.$$

Hence the normalized orthogonal polynomials are

$$\hat{L}_n^{(m)}(x) = \sqrt{\frac{n!}{(m+n)!}}\; L_n^{(m)}(x)\;.$$

Hence we have

$$\hat{L}_0^{(m)}(x) = \sqrt{1/m!}\;,$$

$$\hat{L}_1^{(m)}(x) = \sqrt{1/(m+1)!}\,[-x + (m+1)]\;,$$

$$\hat{L}_2^{(m)}(x) = \sqrt{2/(m+2)!}\,\left[\frac{1}{2}x^2 - (m+2)\,x + \frac{1}{2}(m+2)(m+1)\right]\;,$$

$$\hat{L}_3^{(m)}(x) = \sqrt{6/(m+3)!}\,\left[-\frac{1}{6}x^3 + \frac{1}{2}(m+3)\,x^2 - \frac{1}{2}(m+3)(m+2)\,x\right.$$
$$\left. + \frac{1}{6}(m+3)(m+2)(m+1)\right]\;.$$

5.7 Solution

It is easy to prove, e.g., by induction, that

$$P_n(\cos\theta) = A_n \cos n\theta + A_{n-1}\cos(n-1)\theta + \cdots + A_0$$

where all the A_i are positive. We only need the fact that $2\cos\theta\,\cos r\,\theta = \cos(r+1)\theta + \cos(r-1)\theta$. This result can also be obtained formally using the generating function:

$$\sum t^n P_n(\cos\theta) = \{1 - 2t\cos\theta + t^2\}^{-1/2} = (1 - t\,e^{i\theta})^{-1/2}(1 - t\,e^{-i\theta})^{-1/2}$$
$$= (1 + a_1 t\,e^{i\theta} + a_2 t^2 e^{2i\theta} + \cdots)(1 + a_1 t\,e^{-i\theta} + a_2 t^2 e^{-2i\theta} + \cdots)$$

where all the a_r are positive. The actual values of the A_i can be obtained:

$$P_n(\cos\theta) = \left[\frac{(2n)!}{2^{2n}\,n!\,n!}\left\{\cos n\,\theta + \frac{1}{1}\frac{n}{(2n-1)}\cos(n-2)\theta\right.\right.$$
$$\left.\left. + \frac{1.3}{1.2}\frac{n(n-1)}{(2n-1)(2n-3)}\cos(n-4)\theta + \cdots\right\}\right]\;.$$

Since the A_i are all positive and since the cosines are all in absolute value at most unity, the maximum absolute value of $P_n(\cos\theta)$ cannot exceed $A_n + A_{n-1} + \cdots + A_0$ but this is attained for $\theta = 0$ and we know that $P_n(1) = 1$. [The last result can also be established by induction from the recurrence relation

$$(n+1)P_{n+1}(z) = (2n+1)\,z\,P_n(z) - n\,P_{n-1}(z)$$

by putting $z = 1$.]

5.8   Solution

We take the case of $P_n(x)$ only. We first show that

$$I_{m,n} = \int_{-1}^{+1} P_m'(x)\, P_n'(x)\, (1 - x^2)\, dx = 0 \quad \text{if} \quad m \neq n .$$

If $m \neq n$ we may suppose $m < n$. Then inserting the Rodrigues expressions for $P_m'(x)$, $P_n'(x)$ and integrating by parts once we find

$$2^{m+n} \times m!\, n!\, I_{m,n} = \left[D^n(x^2 - 1)^n \times (1 - x^2)\, D^{m+1}(x^2 - 1)^m \right]_{-1}^{+1}$$

$$- \int_{-1}^{+1} D^n(x^2 - 1)^n\, \{ D[(1 - x^2)\, D^{m+1}(x^2 - 1)^m] \}\, dx$$

so that

$$2^m \times m!\, I_{m,n}$$

$$= - \int_{-1}^{+1} P_n(x)\, \{ - 2\, x\, D^{m+1}(x^2 - 1)^m + (1 - x^2)\, D^{m+2}(x^2 - 1)^m \}\, dx .$$

The degree of the expression $\{\cdots\}$ does not exceed m: the integral therefore vanishes by orthogonality.

If $m = n$ we obtain, similarly

$$2^n (n!)^n\, I_{n,n} = - \int_{-1}^{+1} P_n(x)\, \{ - 2\, x\, D^{n+1}(x^2 - 1)^n + (1 - x^2)\, D^{n+2}(x^2 - 1)^n \}\, dx .$$

From the differential equation for P_n we find

$$\{ \cdots \}/2^n \times n! = - 2\, x\, P_n'(x) + (1 - x^2)\, P_n''(x) = - n(n + 1)\, P_n(x) .$$

Hence

$$I_{n,n} = n(n + 1) \int_{-1}^{+1} P_n^2(x)\, dx = \frac{2\, n\, (n + 1)}{2\, n + 1} .$$

More generally it can be shown that, superscripts denoting differentiation,

$$\int_{-1}^{+1} P_m^{(r)}(x)\, P_n^{(r)}(x)\, (1 - x^2)^r\, dx = \frac{2\, (n + r)!}{(2\, n + 1)\, (n - r)!}\, \delta(m, n) .$$

5.9   Solution

We prove that

$$\sum = \sum_{k=1}^{n} (- 1)^k \cos(k\, m\, \pi/(n + 1)) = \tfrac{1}{2} \{ (- 1)^{n+m} - 1 \} ,$$

if $m = 0, 1, \ldots, n$, i.e., Σ is zero if n, m have the same parity and is otherwise -1. If $m = n + 1$ it is clear that $\Sigma = \Sigma (-1)^k (-1)^k = n + 1$. We can write the general term as

$$\cos k \pi (1 + \{m/(n + 1)\})$$

and apply the elementary result

$$\cos \alpha + \cos 2\alpha + \cdots + \cos n\alpha = \frac{\sin \frac{1}{2} n\alpha \cos \frac{1}{2} (n + 1)\alpha}{\sin \frac{1}{2}\alpha}$$

to find

$$\Sigma = \frac{\sin \frac{1}{2} n\pi \left(1 + \frac{m}{n + 1}\right) \cos \frac{1}{2}\pi (n + 1 + m)}{\sin \frac{1}{2}\pi \left(1 + \frac{m}{n + 1}\right)}.$$

Distinguishing the cases $n + m$ even and then $n + m \equiv 1(4)$ and $n + m \equiv -1(4)$ we obtain the result announced.

5.10   Solution

The sum in question, Σ_r, is zero for $r = 0, 1, \ldots, n - 1$ and 2^{1-n} for $r = n$. This can be deduced from the preceding result since we have

$$2^{n-1} \cos^n \theta = \cos n\theta + n \cos (n - 2) \theta + \cdots.$$

(Take care of the coefficient of the last term.) We have

$$\Sigma_r = \frac{2^{-r}}{r + 1} \sum_{k=0}^{n} (-1)^{k+1} \left[\left\{ \cos \frac{(k + 1)(r + 1)\pi}{n + 1} - \cos \frac{k(r + 1)\pi}{n + 1} \right\} \right.$$

$$+ (r + 1) \left\{ \cos \frac{(k + 1)(r - 1)\pi}{n + 1} - \cos \frac{k(r - 1)\pi}{n + 1} \right\} + \cdots \left. \right].$$

We note that

$$\sum_{k=0}^{n} (-1)^k \left\{ \cos \frac{(k + 1) m\pi}{n + 1} - \cos \frac{k m\pi}{n + 1} \right\}$$

$$= 2 \sum_{k=1}^{n} (-1)^k \cos \frac{k m\pi}{n + 1} + 1 + (-1)^{n+1} \cos m\pi$$

(separating the first and last terms)

$$= (-1)^{n+m} - 1 + 1 + (-1)^{n+1} (-1)^m$$

(by **Problem 5.9**,   if $m = 0, 1, 2, \ldots, n$)

$$= 0.$$

Hence the contributions of all the terms in braces $\{\cdots\}$ to Σ_r vanish if $r + 1 \leq n$, but if $r = n$ there is a contribution from the initial term only. We therefore have $\Sigma_r = 0$, if $r = 0, 1, \ldots, n - 1$ and

$$\Sigma_n = \frac{2^{-n}}{n+1} \sum_{k=0}^{n} (-1)^{k+1} \left[\cos (k+1)\,\pi - \cos k\,\pi\right]$$

$$= \frac{2^{-n}}{n+1} \sum_{k=0}^{n} 2$$

$$= 2^{1-n} .$$

5.11 Solution

We have seen that $\max | P_n(x) | = 1$. (**Problem 5.7**). So $\max | \tilde{P}_n(x) | = 2^n (n!)^2/(2n!)$ while $\max | \tilde{T}_n(x) | = 2^{1-n}$. The ratio (necessarily greater than unity) is:

$$\frac{2^n (n!)^2}{(2n)!\; 2^{1-n}} = \sqrt{\left\{\frac{2^{4n} (n!)^4}{(2n!)^2 \times (2n+1)}\right\} \frac{2n+1}{4}} .$$

The term in braces, by WALLIS' Formula, approaches $\pi/2$. Hence the ratio is asymptotically $\sqrt{\pi n/4}$.

On the other hand, we have

$$\int_{-1}^{+1} P_n^2(x)\, dx = \frac{2}{2n+1}$$

so that

$$\int_{-1}^{+1} \tilde{P}_n^2(x)\, dx = \left(\frac{2^n (n!)^2}{(2n!)}\right)^2 \times \frac{2}{2n+1}$$

and

$$\int_{-1}^{+1} T_n^2(x)\, dx = 1 - \frac{1}{4n^2 - 1}$$

so that

$$\int_{-1}^{+1} \tilde{T}_n^2(x)\, dx = 2^{-2n+2}\left(1 - \frac{1}{4n^2 - 1}\right) .$$

The ratio of these quantities is

$$\frac{2^{-2n+2}\left(1 - \dfrac{1}{4n^2 - 1}\right)}{\left(\dfrac{2^n (n!)^2}{(2n!)}\right)^2 \times \dfrac{2}{2n+1}} \sim \frac{4}{\pi}$$

(by using WALLIS' Formula).

Todd 8

5.12   Solution

(i) $\pi_n(x)/(x - x_i)(x - x_j)$ is a polynomial of degree $n - 2$ and so

$$\int_a^b \pi_n(x) \{\pi_n(x)/(x - x_i)(x - x_j)\} w(x)\, dx = 0, \quad \text{i.e.,} \quad (l_i, l_j) = 0\ .$$

(ii) $\sum l_i(x) \equiv 1$ by the fundamental Lagrangian formula. Hence

$$\int_a^b \{\sum l_i(x)\}^2\, w(x)\, dx = \int_a^b w(x)\, dx$$

but the left hand side is just

$$\sum \int_a^b \{l_i(x)\}^2\, w(x)\, dx + 2 \sum_{i < j} \int_a^b l_i(x)\, l_i(j)\, w(x)\, dx$$

and the second term is zero by (i).

5.16—5.19   Solutions   [See MURNAGHAN and WRENCH (1959)].

In connection with **Problem 5.17**, use is made of the expansion due to JACOBI:

$$\cos(z \cos x) = J_0(x) + 2 \sum_{n = 1}^\infty (-1)^n\, J_{2n}(z)\, T_{2n}(x)\ .$$

There is a similar expansion for $\sin(z \cos x)$:

$$\sin(z \cos x) = 2 \sum_{n = 0}^\infty (-1)^n\, J_{2n+1}(z)\, T_{2n+1}(x)\ .$$

The coefficients $J_n(\pi/2)$ have been tabulated by BOOTH (1955).

CHAPTER 6

6.6   Solution

$$f(x) \equiv (4\ x - 3)^3 .$$

$$f^{(1)}(x_3) = 1099 , \quad f^{(2)}(x_3) = 415 , \quad f^{(3)}(x_3) = 343 .$$

6.7   Solution

This is a table of

$$f(x) = (9 + 2\ x)^3 + (9 + 2\ x)^2 + (9 + 2\ x) - 2954 \quad \text{and} \quad f(2.5) = 0 .$$

$$- 1491$$

$$- 575 \qquad - 117$$

$$+ 661 \qquad + 123 \qquad + 3$$

$$+ 2265 \qquad + 387 \qquad + 9 \qquad 0 .$$

6.8   Solution

$$f(x) \equiv (4\ x + 1)^3 - 343, \quad f(1.5) = 0 .$$

The inverse of a polynomial is a polynomial only when it is linear.

− 342	0			
− 218	1	2.7581		
386	2	2.9396	2.1018	
1854	3	2.4672	2.5171	1.9926 .

6.9   Solution

In general,

$$f(x) - L_{n-1}(f,\ x) = f^{(n)}(\zeta)\ (x - x_0)\ (x - x_1) \cdots (x - x_{n-1})/n! .$$

If the x_i are the zeros of $T_n(x)$ then, in general,

$$\left| f(x) - L_{n-1}(f,\ x) \right| \le \max \left| f^{(n)}(\zeta) \right| \max \left| \tilde{T}_n(x) \right| /n! .$$

In our case, since $\left| \tilde{T}_n(x) \right| \le 2^{1-n}$ if $-1 \le x \le 1$, we have

$$\left| f(x) - L_{10}(f,\ x) \right| \le 2^{-9}/10! \doteq 5 \times 10^{-10} .$$

(i)   Since $\left|U_n(x)\right| \leq n+1$ for $-1 \leq x \leq 1$ and since $\tilde{U}_n(x) = 2^{-n}\,U_n(x)$

we have in this case

$$\left|f(x) - L_{10}(f,\,x)\right| \leq 11 \times \frac{2^{-10}}{10\,!} \doteq 3 \times 10^{-9}\,.$$

(ii)   Since $\left|P_n(x)\right| \leq 1$ for $-1 \leq x \leq 1$ and since

$$\tilde{P}_n(x) = \left\{\frac{2^n (n\,!)^2}{(2\,n)\,!}\right\} P_n(x)$$

we have in this case

$$\left|f(x) - L_{10}(f,\,x)\right| \leq \{2^{10}(10\,!)^2/(20\,!)\}/10\,! \doteq 1.5 \times 10^{-9}\,.$$

(iii)   This is not so easy since we have no convenient inequalities available for the polynomial

$$\left(x^2 - 1\right)\left(x^2 - (49/81)\right)\left(x^2 - (25/81)\right)\left(x^2 - (1/9)\right)\left(x^2 - (1/81)\right).$$

Reference to standard tables [NATIONAL BUREAU OF STANDARDS (1948), p. xvi] shows that the maximum value of this in $-1 \leq x \leq 1$ is about $0.01 \times (2/9)^{10} \times 10!$. Hence

$$\left|f(x) - L_{10}(f,\,x)\right| \leq 3 \times 10^{-9}\,.$$

6.10   Solution

The correct value is

$$J_0(1.45) = 0.539541\ 2804\,.$$

Linear interpolation gives

$$J_0(1.45) = 0.539\textbf{341}\ \textbf{3960}$$

while the Hermite process gives

$$J_0(1.45) = 0.539541\ \textbf{2559}\,.$$

[For further discussions of this process see e.g. SALZER (1959).]

CHAPTER 7

7.1   Solution

$$\frac{1}{2} t \cot \frac{1}{2} t = \sum_{0}^{\infty} (-1)^n \frac{B_{2n}}{(2n)!} t^{2n}, \quad |t| < 2\pi$$

$$\tan \frac{1}{2} t = \sum_{1}^{\infty} (-1)^{n+1} \frac{2(2^{2n}-1) B_{2n} t^{2n-1}}{(2n)!}, \quad |t| < \pi$$

$$\sec t = \sum_{0}^{\infty} (-1)^n t^{2n} E_{2n}/(2n)!, \quad |t| < \pi/2.$$

7.2   Solution

The *estimated* errors are

$$\begin{array}{llll}
\text{for} & n = 10, & \text{at most} & (12 \times 9\tfrac{1}{2})^{-1} < 0.01, \\
\text{for} & n = 100, & \text{at most} & (12 \times 99\tfrac{1}{2})^{-1} < 0{,}001, \\
\text{for} & n = 1000, & \text{at most} & (12 \times 999\tfrac{1}{2})^{-1} < 0.0001.
\end{array}$$

Now

$$\log 100! = 157.97000 \cdots \times 2.3025851 \cdots = 363.73937 \ldots$$

whereas our formula gives $363.73843\ldots$, an *actual* error of 0.00094, so our estimate is a very good one.

7.3   Solution

A naive approach to this problem indicates that the remainder after n terms is $O(n^{-1})$. We use

$$\sum_{0}^{\infty} f(n) = \int_{0}^{\infty} f(x)\, dx + \frac{1}{2} f(0) - \frac{1}{12} f'(0) + \frac{1}{720} f'''(0) - \cdots.$$

We have

$$(1 + 2^{-2} + \cdots + 9^{-2}) = \quad 1.549\ 767\ 7312,$$

$$\int_{0}^{\infty} (10 + x)^{-2}\, dx = \quad 0.100000\ 0000$$

$$+ \frac{1}{2} \times 10^{-2} \quad + 0.005000\ 0000$$

$$+ \frac{1}{12} \times (2!) \times 10^{-3} \quad + 0.000166\ 6667$$

$$- \frac{1}{720} \times (4!) \times 10^{-5} \quad - 0.000000\ 3333$$

$$+ \frac{1}{30\ 240} \times (6!) \times 10^{-7} \quad + 0.000000\ 0024.$$

Hence

$$\sum_{1}^{\infty} n^{-2} = 1.644934\ 0670$$

which is to be compared with

$$\pi^2/6 = 1.644934\ 0668.$$

CHAPTER 8

8.1   Solution

Suppose false and that $\sum \lambda_i b_i$ and $\sum \lambda_i' b_i$ were *distinct* best approximations to f. Then

$$\left\| f - \sum \lambda_i b_i \right\| = \left\| f - \sum \lambda_i' b_i \right\| = \mu \,.$$

(We may assume $\mu > 0$, for if not f is a linear combination of the b_i and uniqueness follows from their independence.) Write

$$\lambda_i'' = \frac{1}{2}\,(\lambda_i + \lambda_i') \,.$$

Then, by the triangle inequality,

$$\left\| f - \sum \lambda_i'' b_i \right\| = \left\| \frac{1}{2}\,(f - \sum \lambda_i b_i) + \frac{1}{2}\,(f - \sum \lambda_i' b_i) \right\| \le \frac{1}{2}\,\mu + \frac{1}{2}\,\mu = \mu \,.$$

Since μ is the minimum we have

$$\left\| f - \sum \lambda_i'' b_i \right\| = \mu \,.$$

This means that

$$\left\| f - \sum \lambda_i'' b_i \right\| = \left\| \frac{1}{2}\,(f - \sum \lambda_i b_i) \right\| + \left\| \frac{1}{2}\,(f - \sum \lambda_i' b_i) \right\|$$

and because of the hypothesis

$$f - \sum \lambda_i b_i = k\left\{ f - \sum \lambda_i' b_i \right\} \,.$$

Then if $k \ne 1$, f is a linear combination of the b_i and $\mu = 0$, in contradiction to our assumption. Hence $\sum (\lambda_i - \lambda_i')\, b_i = 0$, which implies that the b_i are dependent, in contradiction with our assumption.

8.3   Solution

(a)   Since

$$|Q(f)| = \left| \sum a_i f(x_i) \right| \le \sum |a_i|\,|f(x_i)|$$

$$\le \max |f(x_i)| \sum |a_i|$$

$$\le \|f\| \sum |a_i|$$

we have

$$\|Q\| \le \sum |a_i| \,.$$

Consider, however, a function $f(x)$ which is continuous in $[a, b]$ and assumes the value $(\operatorname{sign} a_i)$ at a_i, $i = 1, 2, \ldots, n$. Then $\|f(x)\| = 1$ and $|\sum a_i f(x_i)| = \sum |a_i|$.

Hence

$$\| Q \| \geq \sum | a_i |$$

It follows that $\| Q \| = \sum | a_i |$.

(b) Since

$$| I(f) | = \left| \int_a^b f(x) \, w(x) \, dx \right| \leq \| f \| \int_a^b w(x) \, dx$$

$$= \| f \| \, \mu_0$$

where

$$\mu_0 = \int_a^b w(x) \, dx \, ,$$

we have

$$\| I \| \leq \mu_0 \, .$$

Consider, however, the function $f(x) \equiv 1$ in $[a, b]$. Then $\| f(x) \| = 1$, $| I | = \mu_0$. Hence

$$\| I \| \geq \mu_0 \, .$$

It follows that $\| I \| = \mu_0$.

CHAPTER 9

9.1   Solution

This is merely a translation of the Gaussian quadrature associated with $P_3(x) = 5\,x^3 - 3\,x$. We have seen

$$\int_{-1}^{+1} f(x)\,dx = \sum \lambda_i\, f(x_i)$$

where $x_i = 0,\ \pm\sqrt{3/5}$ and where we may calculate the λ_i either from (9.4), or from (9.9). We use the first method.

$$\lambda_i = \int_{-1}^{+1} l_i^2(x)\,dx$$

where $l_i(x)$ is a quadratic for which $\lambda_i(x_j) = \delta(i, j)$. This means

$$l_1(x) = -\frac{5}{3}\left(x^2 - \frac{3}{5}\right),\quad l_2(x) = \frac{5}{6}\left(x^2 - \sqrt{\frac{3}{5}}\,x\right),\quad l_3(x) = \frac{5}{6}\left(x^2 + \sqrt{\frac{3}{5}}\,x\right).$$

Squaring and integrating, noting the odd powers in $l_i(x)$ make no contribution, we find

$$\lambda_1 = \frac{25}{9}\left[\frac{x^5}{5} - \frac{2\,x^3}{5} + \frac{9\,x}{25}\right]_{-1}^{+1} = \frac{8}{9},$$

$$\lambda_2 = \lambda_3 = \frac{25}{36}\left[\frac{x^5}{5} + \frac{x^3}{5}\right]_{-1}^{+1} = \frac{5}{9}.$$

The corresponding result required is

$$\int_a^b f(x)\,dx = (b - a)\sum \lambda_i\, f(x_i)$$

where $x_i = \frac{1}{2}(a + b) + \frac{1}{2}(b - a)\,t_i$ and where t_i is a zero of $P_4(x) \equiv 35\,x^4 - 30\,x^2 + 3$ and where

$$\lambda_i = \frac{9}{1 - t_i^2} \times \frac{1}{[P_4'(t_i)]^2}.$$

Actually

$$t_i = \pm\,0.33998\,,\quad \pm\,0.86114\,,$$

$$\lambda_i = \quad 0.32607\,,\quad\quad 0.17393\,.$$

[Cf. NAUTICAL ALMANAC OFFICE (1956), p. 67.]

9.5   Solution

By (9.3) we have

$$f(b) - f(a) = \int_a^b f'(x)\, dx = \sum_{i=1}^n \lambda_i f'(x_i)$$

where $\sum \lambda_i = (b - a)$, and where $x_i = \frac{1}{2}(a + b) + \frac{1}{2}(b - a) z_i$, the z_i being the zeros of $P_n(x)$. By **(9.3)** the λ_i are positive.

$\sum \lambda_i f'(x_i)/(b - a)$ is a mean among the values of the $f'(x_i)$ and is therefore equal to $f'(\zeta)$ for a suitable ζ in the range.

9.6   Solution

The relevant abscissas $x_i^{(5)}$ and weights $A_i^{(5)}$ are:

$$x_1^{(5)} = 0.263560\ 319718\,, \quad A_1^{(5)} = 0.521755\ 610583\,,$$
$$x_2^{(5)} = 1.413403\ 059107\,, \quad A_2^{(5)} = 0.398666\ 811083\,,$$
$$x_3^{(5)} = 3.596425\ 771041\,, \quad A_3^{(5)} = 0.075942\ 4496817\,,$$
$$x_4^{(5)} = 7.085810\ 005859\,, \quad A_4^{(5)} = 0.003611\ 758679\ 92\,,$$
$$x_5^{(5)} = 12.640800\ 844276\,, \quad A_5^{(5)} = 0.000023\ 369972\ 3858\,.$$

$$I \doteq Q_5 = e^{-10} \sum A_i/(10 + x_i)$$

We find

$$Q_5 = 0.091563\ 3319 \times e^{-10}$$

which is to be compared with the correct value

$$e^{10} E_1(10) = 0.091563\ 334\,.$$

For developments of this problem see TODD (1954).

9.7   Solution

Let p^*_{2n-1} be the polynomial of best approximation to f. Then, considering R as a linear functional

$$|R(f)| = |R(f - p^*_{2n-1})| \le \|R\| \, \|f - p^*_{2n-1}\|$$
$$= \|R\| \, E_{2n-1}(f)$$
$$\le \left(\sum_{r=1}^n \lambda_r + \int_a^b w(x)\, dx \right) E_{2n-1}(f)$$
$$= 2\,\mu_0\, E_{2n-1}(f)\,.$$

The second inequality follows by use of the results of **Problem 8.3**.

This result is actually a special case of a duality theorem. [See Corollary 2 in RIVLIN and SHAPIRO (1961)].

Research Problem: What is the corresponding result for infinite intervals?

9.8   Solution

This is SIMPSON's Rule. Since the quadrature is not of Lagrangian type the usual error estimate is not applicable; one can be obtained as follows:

We apply the relation

$$\int u\, v^{(3)}\, dt = u\, v'' - u'\, v' + u''\, v - \int u^{(3)}\, v\, dt$$

to the case

$$u = \frac{1}{6}\, x(1-x)^2\,, \quad v = f(x) + f(-x)\,.$$

We find, since $u^{(3)} = 1$,

$$\int_{-1}^{+1} f(t)\, dt = \frac{1}{3}\,[f(1) + 4\, f(0) + f(+1)] - \int_{0}^{1} u\, v^{(3)}\, dt\,.$$

Assuming the existence of $f^{(4)}(t)$ we have

$$f^{(3)}(x) - f^{(3)}(-x) = 2\, x\, f^{(4)}(\zeta)\,, \quad -x \le \zeta \le x\,.$$

Hence, if $|\,f^{(4)}(x)\,| \le M_4, -1 \le x \le 1$ we have the following estimate for $I - Q$:

$$|\,I - Q\,| \le 2\, M_4 \int_{0}^{1} x^2(1-x)^2\, dx/6 = M_4/90\,.$$

BIBLIOGRAPHY

ACHIESER, N. I. (1953), *Vorlesungen über Approximationstheorie* (Akademie-Verlag, Berlin).

APOSTOL, T. M. (1957), *Mathematical Analysis* (Addison-Wesley, Reading, Mass.).

BERNSTEIN, S. (1926), *Leçons sur les propriétés extrémales et la meilleure approximation des fonctions analytiques d'une variable réelle* (Gauthier-Villars, Paris).

BIRKHOFF, G., and MACLANE, S. (1953), *A Survey of Modern Algebra* (MacMillan, New York, N. Y.).

BOOTH, A. D. (1955), *A Note on Approximating Polynomials for Trigonometric Functions*, Math. Tables Aids Comput. *9*, 21–23.

BRITISH ASSOCIATION MATHEMATICAL TABLES (1946), Part-volume A: *Legendre Polynomials* (University Press, Cambridge).

BUCK, R. C. (1959), *Linear Spaces and Approximation Theory*, pp. 11–23, in LANGER (1959).

BUCK, R. C. (1961), Editor, *MAA Studies in Mathematics: I, Studies in Modern Analysis*, (Prentice-Hall, Inc., Englewood Cliffs, N. J.).

BURKILL, J. C. (1959), *Lectures on Approximation by Polynomials* (Tata Institute, Bombay).

CLENSHAW, C. W. (1962), *Chebyshev Series for Mathematical Functions*, National Physical Laboratory, Mathematical Tables, vol. 5 (H. M. Stationery Office, London).

CLENSHAW, C. W., and OLVER, F. W. J. (1955), *The Use of Economized Polynomials in Mathematical Tables*, Proc. Cambridge Phil. Soc. *51*, 614–628.

DAVIS, P. J. (1963), *Interpolation and Approximation* (Ginn & Co., Boston).

DAVIS, P. J., and RABINOWITZ, P. (1956), *Abscissas and Weights for Gaussian Quadratures of High Order*, J. Res. Nat. Bur. Standards *56*, 35–37.

DAVIS, P. J., and RABINOWITZ, P. (1958), *Abscissas and Weights for Gaussian Quadratures of High Order: Values for n = 64, 80 and 96*, J. Res. Nat. Bur. Standards *60*, 613–614.

DE RHAM, G. (1957), *Sur un exemple de fonction continue sans dérivée*, Enseignement Math. *3*, (2), 71–72.

DUFFIN, R. J., and SCHAEFFER, A. C. (1941), *A Refinement of an Inequality of the Brothers Markoff*, Trans. Amer. Math. Soc. *50*, 517–528.

ERDÉLYI, A., et al. (1953), *Higher Transcendental Functions*, I, II (McGraw-Hill Book Co., Inc., New York, N. Y.).

ERDÖS, P., and TURÁN, P., (1937) *On Interpolation*, I, Ann. of Math. *38*, 142–155.

FOX, L. (1956), *The Use and Construction of Mathematical Tables*, National Physical Laboratory, Mathematical Tables, vol. 1 (H. M. Stationery Office, London).

FRÉCHET, M. (1920), *Sur un défaut de la méthode d'interpolation par les polynomes de Lagrange*, Nouv. Ann. de Math. *20*, 241–249.

HASTINGS, C. (1955), *Approximations for Digital Computers* (Princeton University Press, Princeton, N. J.).

HOCHSTRASSER, U. W. (1962), *Orthogonal polynomials*, Ch. 22 in National Bureau of Standards (1963).

HORNECKER, G. (1958), *Evaluation approché de la meilleure approximation polynomiale d'ordre n de f(x) sur un segment fini [a, b]*, Chiffres *1*, 157–169.

JAHNKE, E., EMDE, F., and LÖSCH, F. (1960), *Tables of Higher Functions* (McGraw-Hill Book Co., Inc., New York, N. Y.).

JONES, C. W., MILLER, J. C. P., CONN, J. F. C., and PANKHURST, R. C. (1946), *Tables of Chebyshev Polynomials*, Proc. Roy. Soc. Edinburgh [A], *52*, 187–203.

KARMAZINA, L. N. (1954), *Tables of Jacobi Polynomials* (Akad. Nauk SSSR, Moscow).

KNOPP, K. (1928), *Theory and Application of Infinite Series* (Blackie & Son, Ltd., London).

KOPAL, Z. (1962), *Numerical Analysis* (John Wiley & Sons, Inc., New York, N. Y.).

LANCZOS, C. (1938), *Trigonometric Interpolation of Empirical and Analytical Functions*, J. Math. Phys. *17*, 123–199.

LANCZOS, C. (1956), *Applied Analysis* (Prentice-Hall, Inc., Englewood Cliffs, N. J.).

LANDAU, E. (1950), *Differential and Integral Calculus* (Chelsea Publishing Co., New York N. Y.).

LANGER, R. E. (1959), Editor, *On Numerical Approximation* (University of Wisconsin Press, Madison, Wisconsin).

LEVIT, R. J. (1963), *The Finite Difference Extension of Rolle's Theorem*, Amer. Math. Monthly *70*, 26–30.

LITTLEWOOD, J. E. (1953), *A Mathematician's Miscellany* (Methuen, London).

LORENTZ, G. G. (1953), *Bernstein Polynomials* (University of Toronto Press, Toronto).

LOWAN, A. N., DAVIDS, N., and LEVENSON, A. (1942), *Table of the Zeros of the Legendre Polynomials, etc.* pp. 185–189 in National Bureau of Standards (1954).

MAGNUS, W., and OBERHETTINGER, F. (1948), *Formeln und Sätze für die speziellen Funktionen der mathematischen Physik* (Springer-Verlag, Göttingen).

MUNCH, O. J. (1960), *On Some Inequalities by W. A. Markoff*, Nordisk Math. Tid. *2*, 21–29, 63–64.

MURNAGHAN, F. D., and WRENCH, J. W., JR. (1959), *The Determination of the Chebyshev Approximating Polynomials for a Differentiable Function*, Math. Tables Aids Comput, *13*, 185–193.

NATANSON, I. P. (1955), *Konstruktive Funktionentheorie* (Akademie-Verlag, Berlin).

NATANSON, I. P. (1961), *Constructive Theory of Functions* (Office of Technical Services, U.S. Dept. of Commerce, Washington, 25, D.C.).

NATIONAL BUREAU OF STANDARDS (1948), *Tables of Lagrangian Interpolation Coefficients* (Columbia University Press, New York, N. Y.).

NATIONAL BUREAU OF STANDARDS (1952), *Tables of Chebyshev Polynomials*, Applied Mathematics Series, vol. 9 (U. S. Government Printing Office, Washington, D. C.).

NATIONAL BUREAU OF STANDARDS (1954), *Tables of Functions and of Zeros of Functions*, Applied Mathematics Series, vol. 37 (U. S. Government Printing Office, Washington, D. C.).

NATIONAL BUREAU OF STANDARDS (1963), *Handbook of Functions*, Applied Mathematics Series, vol. 55 (U. S. Government Printing Office, Washington, D. C.).

NATIONAL PHYSICAL LABORATORY (1961), *Modern Computing Methods* (H. M. Stationery Office, London).

H. M. NAUTICAL ALMANAC OFFICE (1956), *Interpolation and Allied Tables* (H. M. Stationery Office, London).

OSTROWSKI, A. M. (1952–1954), *Vorlesungen über Differential- und Integralrechnung*, Bd. 1, **2**, **3** (Birkhäuser Verlag, Basel).

PÓLYA, G., and SZEGÖ, G. (1925), *Aufgaben und Lehrsätze aus der Analysis*, I, II (Springer-Verlag, Berlin).

RABINOWITZ, P., and WEISS, G. (1959), *Tables of Abscissas and Weights for Numerical Evaluation of Integrals of the Form $\int_0^{\infty} e^{-x} x^n f(x)\, dx$*, Math. Tables Aids Comput. *13*, 285–294.

RIVLIN, T. J. (1962), *Polynomials of Best Uniform Approximation to Certain Rational Functions*, Numer. Math., *4*, 345–349.

RIVLIN, T. J., and SHAPIRO, H. S. (1961), *A Unified Approach to Certain Problems of Approximation and Minimization*, J. Soc. Indust. Appl. Math. *9*, 670–699.

ROGOSINSKI, W. W. (1955), *Some Elementary Inequalities for Polynomials*, Math. Gaz. *39*, 7–12.

SALZER, H. E. (1959), *Tables of Osculatory Interpolation Coefficients*, National Bureau of Standards Applied Mathematics Series, vol. 56 (U. S. Government Printing Office, Washington, D. C.).

SALZER, H. E., and ZUCKER, R. (1949), *Table of the Zeros and Weight Factors of the First Fifteen Laguerre Polynomials*, pp. 191–199 in National Bureau of Standards (1954).

SALZER, H. E., ZUCKER, R., and CAPUANO, R. (1952), *Table of the Zeros and Weight Factors of the First Twenty Hermite Polynomials*, J. Res. Nat. Bur. Standards *48*, 111–116.

SANSONE, G. (1959), *Orthogonal Functions* (tr. A. H. Diamond, Interscience Publishers Inc., New York, N. Y.).

SCHEID, F. (1961), *The Over-under-over Theorem*, Amer. Math. Monthly *68*, 862–871.

SLATER, L. J. (1956), *A Short Table of Laguerre Polynomials*, Proc. Inst. Elec. Engrs. [C], *103*, 46–50.

STIEFEL, E. L. (1959), *Numerical Methods in Tchebycheff Approximation*, pp. 217–232 in LANGER (1959).

STIEFEL, E. L. (1960), *Note on Jordan Elimination, Linear Programming and Tchebycheff Approximation*, Numer. Math. *2*, 1–17.

STIEFEL, E. L. (1961), *Einführung in die numerische Mathematik* (B. G. Teubner Verlagsgesellschaft, Stuttgart).

STONE, M. H. (1948), *The Generalized Weierstrass Approximation Theorem*, pp. 123–456 in BUCK (1961).

SZEGÖ, G. (1959), *Orthogonal Polynomials* (American Mathematical Society, Providence, R. I.).

TALBOT, A. (1962), *On a Class of Tchebysheffian Approximation Problems Solvable Algebraically*, Proc. Cambridge Phil. Soc. *58*, 244–267.

TODD, J. (1954), *Evaluation of the Exponential Integral for large Complex Arguments*, J. Res. Nat. Bur. Standards *52*, 313–317.

TODD, J. (1962), *The Constructive Theory of Functions*, Ch. 3 in *A Survey of Numerical Analysis* (McGraw-Hill Book Co., Inc., New York, N. Y.).

VISSER, C. (1945), *A Simple Proof of Certain Inequalities for Polynomials*, Nederl. Akad. Wetensch. Proc. [A], *48*, 276–285.

WIENER, N. (1949), *Extrapolation, Interpolation and Smoothing of Stationary Time Series* (John Wiley & Sons, Inc., New York, N. Y.).

INDEX